THE BIOLOGY OF A MARINE COPEPOD

Photo: D. P. WILSON

Female *Calanus finmarchicus* (*helgolandicus* form)

THE BIOLOGY OF
A MARINE COPEPOD

Calanus finmarchicus (Gunnerus)

by

S. M. MARSHALL, D.Sc., F.R.S.E., and
A. P. ORR, M.A., D.Sc., F.R.S.E.
of The Marine Station, Millport

OLIVER & BOYD
EDINBURGH: TWEEDDALE COURT
LONDON: 39A WELBECK STREET, W.1

FIRST PUBLISHED . . . 1955

PRINTED IN GREAT BRITAIN
FOR OLIVER AND BOYD LTD., EDINBURGH
BY ROBERT CUNNINGHAM AND SONS LTD., ALVA

FOREWORD

Calanus finmarchicus is one of the most important members of the zoo-plankton because of its enormous numbers and the part it plays in the conversion of the phytoplankton into protein and fat suitable as food for shoaling fishes, whales and many other animals. Much work has been done on it since its discovery in 1767, and here we have attempted to bring together the large amount of information which has been obtained. The stress in this book however has been laid on the life history and physiology rather than on distribution.

We should like to thank Dr C. M. Yonge, F.R.S., Professor of Zoology in the University of Glasgow, for first suggesting the work and for his encouragement thereafter and also Mr F. S. Russell, F.R.S., Director of the Marine Biological Laboratory, Plymouth, and Dr A. C. Hardy, F.R.S., Linacre Professor of Zoology at Oxford, for useful criticisms of the typescript.

Many members of the marine station staff gave us help and we should like particularly to thank Dr R. B. Pike for preparing some of the original drawings for reproduction and Mr E. Latham and Mrs J. S. Morrison for the trouble they took with the photographs.

Dr J. P. Harding of the British Museum was most helpful in the sections dealing with the early stages in the division of the *Calanus* egg and provided numerous photographs. Dr H. Brattstrøm, Professor of Zoology in the University of Bergen, kindly arranged for us to see Gunnerus' original paper and translated it for us. Dr D. P. Wilson of the Plymouth Laboratory kindly allowed us to use one of his photographs as a frontispiece. We are also much indebted to the following authors for permission to reproduce figures from their published papers: Professor Graham Cannon for Figs. 38 and 39, Dr G. L. Clarke for Figs. 47 and 48, Dr D. T. Gauld for Fig. 41, Professor A. C. Hardy for Fig. 50, Dr M. W. Jepps for Figs. 51, 54, 55 and 58, Miss Esther Lowe for Figs. 6, 7, 8 and 9, Dr A. G. Nicholls for Figs. 29 and 49, Dr C. B. Rees for Fig. 2, Mr F. S. Russell for Fig. 46 and Professor H. H. Ussing for Fig. 30. Our thanks are also due to the following societies and institutions for permission to use figures from their publications; the Company of Biologists; the Marine Biological Association of the United Kingdom from whose journal we have borrowed largely, the Marine Biological Laboratory, Woods Hole, and the Royal Society of Edinburgh; and to the following publishers: the Cambridge University

Press, the Clarendon Press, Messrs Macmillan and Co., the Mayflower Press, Messrs Oliver and Boyd Ltd.; also to the editors and publishers of the following journals: *Meddelelser om Grønland* for Fig. 30, *Archives de Zoologie Expérimentale et Générale* for Fig. 53, *Arbeiten der zoologische Institut, Wien,* for Fig. 22, and *Wissenschaftlichen Untersuchungen der deutschen Meere in Kiel* for Fig. 52.

We are most grateful to the Carnegie Trust for the Universities of Scotland for financial help in publication.

CONTENTS

CHAPTER I

SYSTEMATICS AND DISTRIBUTION

Systematics

THE first marine pelagic copepod to be described was taken from the sea a little south of Hammerfest in northern Norway (Finmark) in 1767 and was called *Monoculus finmarchicus* by its discoverer Gunnerus (1770), bishop of Nideros (Trondheim). His diagnosis is as follows:

'To the INSECTA aptera finally belongs:

MONOCULUS finmarchicus, annulis postice qvinqve; capite obtuso: pedum anteriorum qvatur; posteriorum vero qvinqve paribus: cauda recta, bifida.'

His account of the animal is remarkably accurate considering the simple means at his disposal and is of sufficient general interest to quote in full.* His quaint little sketches are shown in Fig. 1.

'At Rensholmen, which is situated a good Finmarkian mile (a couple of Danish miles and more) south of the harbour of Hammerfest in West Finmark the sea everywhere was crowded with these rather small creatures.

'On filling a bottle with sea water, quite a number of them were captured, and in that way the merchant at Hammerfest, Mr Buch, on my last visit there in June 1767 was so kind as to send them to me living. When out of the water they looked rather shapeless, but when one observed them in their element, especially so long as they were alive, one was able to see, with the naked eye, that they had an oblong body like the prawn (CANCER, *Sqvilla*), equipped with two antennae, at least as long as the body, and a rather short tail, and when observing very carefully, one could see that it was cleft at the end; but feet could hardly be seen. It swam very rapidly, straight forward as well as up and down, and, as usual, with the tail down. In this respect it differed from the sea-fly [amphipod] (CANCER *Pulex*), which it otherwise somewhat resembles; for this always swims upside down mostly obliquely upwards.

'Thereafter I observed it through a small lens, but thereby I did not

* We are grateful to Professor Hans Brattstrøm of Bergen University for making this translation.

I

discover more than before except for two pairs of forelegs, and that one observed more distinctly the cleft of the tail.

'But, by the aid of Cuf's magnifying glass, I observed that it had four pairs of forelegs, consisting of three to four bigger joints. The undermost joints on all the feet bore hairs, as did the antennae, on which they were mostly anteriorly directed. When it swam, the foremost legs turned to the sides and the hindmost backwards. Hence the last could not be observed when it was lying on its belly. On the posterior part of the body five annuli were observed, one for each pair of hind legs. The antennae had many joints, but these were so small that they could not be counted. Each half of the cleft tail was constructed like a fish fin and consisted of rays, which were connected by membranes. The snout was stumpy and not saw-like on its upper side, nor with teeth on the underside. Not the slightest indication of eyes or mouth was observed however carefully one looked for them with the magnifying glass. The body was very transparent, shining, smooth, reddish, and furnished with a skin like that of the prawns and the sea-flies but much thinner than theirs.

'This small creature I have referred to MONOCULUS LINN, as it has most conformity with this genus, especially MONOCULO quadricorni LINN, as this is figured in natural size in the Stockholm Handlinger for the year 1747 and the months of July–September, Tab. III, Fig. 2, though I, as is already stated, was not able to observe any eyes. But as I found no mouth either, which it without doubt has, one has no right to deny the presence of eyes, simply because these were not observed under the magnifying glass. It also has a slight resemblance to the crustaceans, especially the species: Squilla, Pulex and Locusta. But as it has no chelae nor palps, as have the crustacea, it cannot be referred to them.'

It was called *Monoculus* to fit into one of the three genera into which Linnaeus had divided arthropods, but Gunnerus' account was published in a very inaccessible journal and this was responsible for some of the trouble over nomenclature. It was not until nearly 100 years later that it was to settle down with its original specific name, and the half century before that was filled with mistaken identifications and controversy.

In 1776 Müller removed the species to the genus *Cyclops* in the Insecta aptera but in 1785 he thought he had rediscovered the animal itself and he described it again and, ignoring its original specific name, called it *Cyclops longicornis*. His drawing however shows caudal furcae much too long for Gunnerus' species.

In 1819 Leach made the genus *Calanus* for the original form. Why Leach chose this name is uncertain. Calanus was a Jain ascetic, one of a strict and ancient sect which abhorred possessions so much that its members gave up even clothing. He followed in the train of Alexander the Great from India to Baghdad and there walked living into the pyre because his life had become worthless to him through illness. He is said to have murmured each morning an Indian greeting which the Greeks understood as 'Kalan' (perhaps 'Kalyam', i.e. God bless you, lit. 'May it be good') and so called him Kalanos. The outstretched antennules of the copepod may have suggested to Leach some Yogi attitude practised by the ascetic.*

Roussel de Vauzème (1834) described a copepod which he found on a whaling voyage in the southern oceans and called *Cetochilus australis*. It was a good description for that date except that he mistook the bases of the antennary muscles for lateral eyes. His species has not so far been redescribed.

In 1840 Milne-Edwards recognized Gunnerus' *Monoculus finmarchicus* and Müller's *Cyclops longicornis* as different species and put the first in the genus *Calanus*; the second he thought too ill-defined to identify. Since he did not himself see Gunnerus' publication he had no opportunity of comparing it with the description of *Cetochilus* which indeed, because of Roussel de Vauzème's so-called lateral eyes, he put in a different group altogether. Roussel de Vauzème's paper was much more accessible than Gunnerus' and later authors tended to compare their copepods with *Cetochilus* rather than with *Calanus*.

In 1843 Goodsir described a *Cetochilus septentrionalis* from the Firth of Forth, making the same mistake as Roussel de Vauzème about the lateral eyes.

In 1848 Krøyer wrote a paper on these copepods. He did not define the genus *Calanus* but he thought that Gunnerus' *Calanus* and Roussel de Vauzème's *Cetochilus* belonged to the same genus, to which he added another species *Calanus hyperboreus*. Unfortunately his paper was for long ignored by later workers.

Confusion now arose over Müller's mistaken identification. Baird in 1850 rediscovered Müller's *Cyclops longicornis* and took over his wrong identification of it with Gunnerus' form. Although he knew of Leach's name *Calanus* he ignored it and called his species *Temora finmarchica*. Since both Müller and Baird were wrong in identifying '*finmarchicus*' with '*longicornis*' their wrongly given names still stand and *Temora longicornis* is a valid species to-day. Baird however defined the genus *Cetochilus* more closely by saying that all five pairs of swimming feet were alike.

In 1852 Dana confused things still further. He knew that *Cetochilus septentrionalis* was supposed to have lateral eyes but ignored the fact that *C. australis* was supposed to have them too, and removed only the second form to the genus *Calanus*. This would not have mattered so much had

* For this information we are indebted to Dr Betty Heimann.

he recognized the difference between the number of swimming feet in immature and adult; as it was he thought that their number was of no systematic importance and included in *Calanus* a number of widely different genera.

In 1863 Claus had therefore to choose between an ill-defined and ill-described genus *Calanus* and a well described one, *Cetochilus*: he chose the second. He also however continued to use the name *Calanus* for forms which he knew were not closely related to the *Monoculus finmarchicus* for which the genus was founded, and later he even divided the genus into three.

In 1865 Boeck at last redefined the genus *Calanus* clearly (although not so fully as Claus) and united *Calanus* Leach with the *Cetochilus* of Roussel de Vauzème, Baird, Goodsir, Claus and others. He identified *Calanus finmarchicus* with *Cetochilus helgolandicus* Claus.

The name *Cetochilus* gradually fell out of use and in Giesbrecht's great monograph of 1892 (from which most of the above account is taken) the synonymy is cleared up and *Calanus finmarchicus* finally accepted as the name for Gunnerus' copepod.

Claus (1881) himself did not accept this change for he thought that, although its size and place of origin made it probable (though not certain) that Gunnerus' copepod belonged to the same genus as *Cetochilus*, yet Gunnerus' description was not sufficient to distinguish his animal from *Calanus hyperboreus*, nor indeed to identify it satisfactorily at all. Later With (1915) voiced the same objections for the same reasons and also because he said Gunnerus did not mention the red colour usually characteristic of *Calanus*, but he concluded that it was not worth while changing the name again. In the last point he was wrong, for Gunnerus (see p. 2) mentions that the body is of a reddish (rödagtig) colour. Giesbrecht unaccountably omitted this word from his translation (1892, p. 93) which may have misled With. The facts that Gunnerus' drawing shows antennules longer than the body, and that there are five equally developed pairs of swimming feet, combined with its discovery in northern Norway do however limit the possibilities to *Calanus*.

Sømme's (1934) measurements show that the copepodite Stage V of *Calanus finmarchicus* is about the same size as the Stage IV of *C. hyperboreus* (and he mentions that the latter may be present in Norwegian waters in June when Gunnerus' copepod was abundant) but in Stage IV the fifth foot is smaller than the rest and in Gunnerus' drawing it is the same size. Although the sketch is not good enough for certainty to be possible, all the indications point to the copepod being *C. finmarchicus*.

In 1903 Sars revived the name *helgolandicus* for the forms which had a more southerly distribution and had been described from Heligoland by Claus (as *Cetochilus helgolandicus*), by Giesbrecht from the Mediterranean, and by Brady (1883) from the Challenger expedition (both as *Calanus finmarchicus*). The species differs from *C. finmarchicus* by a more pointed head, a slenderer body, shorter caudal rami and, in the male, a considerably longer exopod on the fifth foot. Apart from these characteristics the proportions in various parts of the body differ, e.g. the urosome is about half the length of the metasome in *C. finmarchicus* and more than half in *C. helgolandicus* (from his drawings Sars must have included the caudal setae in this measurement); the caudal rami are longer than the anal somite in the former, scarcely longer in the latter. *C. helgolandicus* was smaller than *C. finmarchicus* in Norwegian waters. Sars did not trace its distribution farther north than the Oslo fjord and the south coast of Norway, where it was plentiful, but Runnstrøm (1932) recorded it in the Herdla and Hjelte fjords, and Rose (1929) still farther north.

Some zoologists (Wilson, 1932; Rose, 1933) accepted Sars' diagnosis, but others (Wolfenden, 1905; Nordgaard, 1905; Farran, 1911) could find no sufficient distinction between the two forms.

With (1915) who studied the copepods from the Danish Ingolf Expedition of 1894-95 made a long series of measurements to see whether he could distinguish the two species. The expedition cruised in northern waters, by Greenland, Iceland, the Faeroes and Jan Mayen and was never south of lat. 60°. It is therefore likely to have been chiefly *C. finmarchicus* that was caught. With found, however, that the sizes and proportions given for both species were included in the great range covered by his copepods and when one feature might seem to identify an animal as belonging to the first, another feature in the same individual might be characteristic of the second species. Even in the male fifth foot there was a considerable range and most of his specimens were intermediate between the two species as diagnosed by Sars.

After With's paper most zoologists ignored any distinction and used *C. finmarchicus* as including *C. helgolandicus*.

In 1949, however, Rees recognized two forms in the North Sea and called one 'helgolandicus' because it agreed in the main with Sars' form although he did not go so far as to call it a distinct species. He recognized that most length measurements are too variable to be useful and based his distinction on the shape of the coxa of the fifth leg (Fig. 2). In the Stage V and female *finmarchicus* the inner edge of this is almost straight and in *helgolandicus* it is distinctly concave. Sars does not draw this limb for *helgolandicus* but the inner edge of the coxa is straight in his drawing of *finmarchicus*. A further distinction in the females and Stage V is that already mentioned by Sars, the more pointed head in *helgolandicus*. Rees says that on picking out females from a tow-netting on this character alone he found them all to be *helgolandicus*.

In the male fifth legs the inner edge of the coxa of both forms is concave but they can be distinguished by the greater asymmetry of *helgolandicus*, described by Sars. The Stage V resemble their respective females but the Stage IV are more variable and are difficult to separate. In most Stage IV *finmarchicus* the coxa of the fifth leg is stumpy and its inner edge is convex and bears about 12 teeth; in *helgolandicus* it is not stumpy, is straight or only slightly convex and bears no teeth. The distinction between 'stumpy' and 'not stumpy' is not clear in Rees's drawings.

Currie (1918), however, in her study of moulting in *Calanus* draws the coxa segment in the fifth foot of Stage IV only slightly convex but it is furnished with from 3 to 18 teeth varying in size and arrangement as well as in number. All these moulted into *finmarchicus* Stage V. Unfortunately it is as yet impossible to distinguish between the two forms at any earlier stage. Mr J. Mauchline, working on *Calanus* from Scottish waters, found that in females the number of teeth on the coxa of the fifth leg increased with the length of the animal in *finmarchicus* but not in *helgolandicus*.

In the North Sea according to Rees *helgolandicus* is larger than *finmarchicus* although the size ranges overlap and this is the opposite of what Sars found. Wimpenny (1937) however, states that *Calanus* from the North Sea (which he supposed to be *finmarchicus*) were smaller than the *Calanus* from either Millport or Plymouth. There is in the North Sea a close resemblance between the life histories of the two forms.

The two forms are present both at Plymouth and in the Clyde sea area. At Plymouth in 1926 (Russell, 1951) *helgolandicus* was predominant; *finmarchicus* occurred only in April, May and June, and the maximum in any one sample was 10%. Of 300 specimens taken in July and August all were *helgolandicus*. Similar results were found in the 1930 catches.

In the Clyde sea area in 1950 to 1952 the population was on the contrary almost all *finmarchicus*. About 5% of *helgolandicus* was present during the winter and spring of 1950-51 but they disappeared during the summer months. In the autumn of 1951 the percentage of *helgolandicus* rose to 32 and in September and October, 1952, almost all *Calanus* caught near the surface were *helgolandicus* although in deep waters the proportion was lower. Conditions were similar in 1953 but with an even larger proportion of *helgolandicus*. Both at Plymouth and in the Clyde area *helgolandicus* was larger than *finmarchicus* and in the Clyde it was noted that their eggs and nauplii were larger too (Fig. 2*a* and *c*). Observations made on 17th September 1951 (see p. 40) indicated that their egg-laying behaviour might be different.

In European waters the *finmarchicus* form does not seem to extend much south of the British Isles but *helgolandicus*, the southern form, is sometimes found much farther north. The reason for the reversal of the usual size

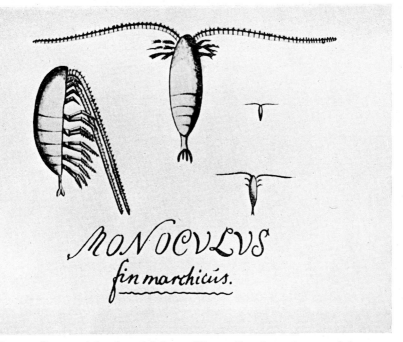

Fig. 1.   Gunnerus' sketches of *Calanus*.   The smallest shows the natural size.

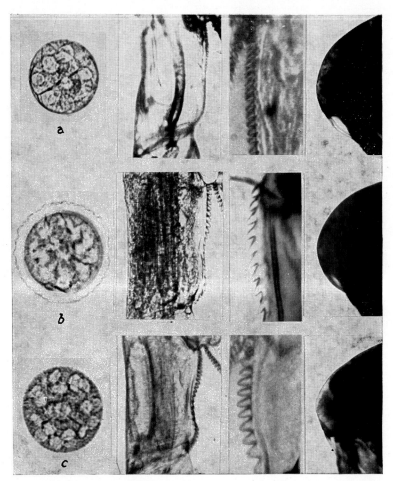

Fig. 2. Typical eggs, the coxa of the left fifth feet, the proximal teeth of the coxa of the right fifth feet and the foreheads of females of (*a*) *Calanus finmarchicus*, (*b*) *Calanus* from Tromsø, and (*c*) *C. helgolandicus*.

relations between southern and northern forms of the same or closely related species may be the fact that *finmarchicus* is near the limit of its range and so perhaps in a rather unfavourable environment. It is a reversal too of the size relationship noted by Sars.

It seems then that Sars was right in distinguishing two forms, but whether these are of specific rank has yet to be decided.

In this book *Calanus finmarchicus* is used in the wide sense to include both forms, except when they have been especially distinguished from one another. In general, work done in Norway north of the Oslo fjord, and in the Clyde sea area, refers to *finmarchicus*, that done at Plymouth to *helgolandicus*. In North America work done on the east coast has probably been with *finmarchicus*; on the west coast the species used is uncertain.

It is possible that there is yet a third form, distinguishable by the eggs, which have a space, rather variable in extent, between the inner and outer egg membranes which appears shortly after the egg is laid, and before the first cleavage. This form was found at Tromsø in the spring of 1952 (Fig. 2b). The diameter of the egg itself (inner membrane) is larger than that of *finmarchicus* and almost as large as *helgolandicus*. With the membrane the diameter may reach 195 μ as against 172 μ for *helgolandicus*. The shape of the coxa on the fifth foot is intermediate between those of *finmarchicus* and *helgolandicus*. (Marshall, Orr and Rees, 1953.)

Calanus belongs to the suborder Gymnoplea of the order Eucopepoda, and *C. finmarchicus* (Gunnerus) is diagnosed as follows:

Head distinct from first thoracic segment. Five free thoracic segments, the corners of the last gently rounded. Caudal rami twice as long as broad. Antennules of 25 segments (in the females) and longer than the body (including urosome) by two or three segments; on the 23rd and 24th segments posteriorly, conspicuous long plumose setae. Exopods of antennae 7-segmented. Endopods of all five pairs of swimming feet 3-segmented. Inner margin of coxa in the fifth pair of swimming feet in the Stage V and female straight with a variable number of teeth, the number decreasing towards the south. In the North Atlantic, for example, there may be up to 40 teeth, near the Azores 27-28 and south of the equator 15-18. Some of the southerly specimens however may be *helgolandicus*. Fifth pair of swimming feet in the male asymmetrical, the right limb the shorter. Endopod of right foot reaching as far or farther than the middle of the second segment of the left exopod. The egg measures about 145 μ (138-151 μ).

The other species in the genus can be distinguished from *C. finmarchicus* (Gunnerus) by the following features:

C. hyperboreus (Krøyer) is considerably larger (female 7-9 mm) and the corners of the last metasome segment are pointed. The row of teeth on the inner margin of the coxa of *p.* 5 does not reach the distal end of the segment. The eggs are large, 200-300 μ and orange-red in colour.

C. helgolandicus (Claus) (see pp. 4-6). The coxa of *p.* 5 in Stage V male and female is slightly convex internally. In the male the endopod of the right *p.* 5 extends only a little beyond the distal margin of the first segment of the exopod. The head is slightly pointed. The eggs are rather larger (av. diam. 172 μ) than those of *C. finmarchicus*.

C. tenuicornis (Dana) is small in size (1·5–1·8 mm). The antennule is one and a half times the length of the whole body. There are no teeth on the inner margin of the coxa in *p.* 5. In the female the genital segment is much produced ventrally.

C. tonsus (Brady). The antennules reach the end of the third urosome segment and have setae only on segments 23, 24 and 25. The 24th segment is twice as long as the 25th. In the female the genital segment is broad and swollen. On the coxae of *p.* 2 and 3 there are four large spines and on the coxa of *p.* 4, 1 or 2; on the coxa of *p.* 5 there are none. In *C. tonsus* var. *plumchrus* (Marukawa) one pair of caudal setae is conspicuously long and plumose.

C. cristatus (Krøyer). The coxa of *p.* 5 is smooth on the internal margin. The head in the frontal region is produced in a crest that projects forward. There are no internal setae on the endopods of *p.* 1-4.

C. propinquus (Brady). The last metasome segment is laterally produced and ends in sharp points. The antennules reach to about the end of the caudal furcae and the setae on segments 23 and 24 are unusually long and thick. In the male the basal joints are much enlarged. The coxa of *p.* 5 is straight on the internal margin and toothed; in the male three of these teeth in a group at the distal end are considerably larger than the others. In the male *p.* 5 the left foot has the endopod reduced so that it reaches only just beyond the distal margin of the 1st exopod segment; the exopod is much longer than that of the right foot. The setae of the antennules and other appendages are often brick red in colour (Verwoort, 1951).

C. simillimus (Giesbrecht). The last metasome segment is the same as in *C. propinquus*. The antennules reach to about the end of the caudal furcae and are faintly brick-red. The coxa of *p.* 5 has a rather convex internal margin and is toothed, with a group of 3 or 4 teeth at the distal end separated from the rest by a small break.

C. pacificus Brodsky is small in size (♀ 2·6 mm, ♂ 2·8 mm). In the male *p.* 5 the endopod of the left leg reaches only to the distal edge of the second segment of the exopod (Brodsky, 1950).

DISTRIBUTION

Calanus is one of those animals whose distribution covers a very large area with temperatures ranging between -2 and $22°$C and salinities between $29°/_{00}$ and $35°/_{00}$. The picture is complicated by the existence of the two forms *finmarchicus* and *helgolandicus* of which the first is cold-loving and northerly, and the second warmth-loving and southerly. As has been mentioned most recent workers have not distinguished the two forms and most of the European records of *C. finmarchicus* south of the English Channel are probably *C. helgolandicus*. Sars said that he had not seen *C. helgolandicus* farther north than the Oslo fjord although it might occur. Rose (1929) who admits that he often finds it difficult to distinguish the two forms, records *C. finmarchicus* from the Mediterranean and off Madeira, and *C. helgolandicus* from as far north as 79°N., the northernmost record for *C. finmarchicus*.

C. finmarchicus has been recorded (With, 1915; Farran, 1911) from all over the North Atlantic (although it is absent in the Baltic and rare in the Kattegat), from the Norwegian, Greenland, Barents and White Seas as far north as 79°N., from the Azores, from the Mediterranean (including the Adriatic) and the Black Sea, but not the Red Sea. Its recorded presence there is, according to Seymour Sewell (1947), an error of transcription, but it is taken, though rarely, in the Indian ocean. It occurs in the South Atlantic, in the Sargasso Sea and as far south as the Cape of Good Hope. Bigelow (1926) states that on the east coast of America its southern limit is about Chesapeake Bay where it is found in winter only. In summer its distribution is limited to the north and in a warm summer it is not found in Chesapeake Bay at all. It is abundant on the Californian coast (Esterly, 1905, 1924) and has been taken on the west coast of South America. Wilson (1942) mentions that in the Pacific it is mostly *C. finmarchicus* which occurs; *C. helgolandicus* was taken only four times during the Pacific cruise of the *Carnegie*. However Esterly's (1905) drawing of the *Calanus* common on the Californian coast is that of a *C. helgolandicus*.

There are also records from the Fiji Islands, Hong Kong, the Malay Archipelago, the south east of Australia in 37°S. and near New Zealand as far south as 50-60°S. Most work on *Calanus* has been done in the northern part of its range and it is probable that some of the records from the Far East and Australasia may be of a different species. Farran (1929) has described differences in the size and spinulation of the coxa of the fifth foot in these southern forms but as we have seen these characters vary too much to be used for specific identification. Mr B. M. Bary of the National Institute of Oceanography (personal communication) has identified the *Calanus* occurring round the S.W. coast of New Zealand as *C. helgolandicus*.

B

In the northern part of its range *C. finmarchicus* is one of the most abundant of copepods occurring often in immense swarms, and it is found at all depths down to 4000 m although most frequently within the top 200 or 300 m. Ussing (1938) indeed thinks that the *Calanus* found in Atlantic abysses have accidentally got too deep to be affected by the light in spring and have been carried south in the deep Arctic current where they are completely lost. Russell (1930*a*) has made a similar suggestion (see, however, pp. 123-124).

It should be mentioned here that a *Calanus* indistinguishable from *C. finmarchicus* (apart from minor size differences) has been described by Stalberg (1931) from the Telezke lake in the Northern Altai mountains, Siberia. About a dozen specimens were found in bottom samples at 18 m, and a few fragments in plankton samples. An independent Russian expedition to the same lake two years later took surface plankton samples but mentions no *Calanus*. This remarkable record needs confirmation (as the author himself recognizes) since *Calanus* has not hitherto been described from fresh water.

CHAPTER II
ANATOMY

IN *Calanus* the body is divided morphologically into a wider and a narrower part, conveniently called the metasome and urosome. The metasome consists of the head (to which is fused the first thoracic somite) and five free thoracic somites. There is an articulation between the fifth free somite and a sixth, on which the genital ducts open. Morphologically this genital somite and the four abdominal somites which follow it, belong to the urosome.

The head bears five pairs of appendages, antennules (or first antennae), antennae (or second antennae), mandibles, maxillules and maxillae. That somite of the thorax which is fused to the head bears a pair of maxillipedes and each of the other thoracic somites has a pair of swimming feet or legs. The urosome has no appendages, but the last somite, on which the anus opens, has a pair of setose projections, the caudal rami.

In the males of most copepods one antennule and the fifth pair of swimming feet are modified, often forming complicated organs for grasping the female during mating and transferring the spermatophore to her genital segment. In the female the fifth legs are often reduced or absent. *Calanus* however is in some ways rather a primitive form; the five thoracic somites are free, the male antennules are little modified and the fifth swimming feet in the male show only a slight asymmetry. The female has the five pairs complete and the fifth is only a little smaller than the fourth. Although the fifth pair is so little modified in the male, Giesbrecht (1892) says that the left leg can be used as a grasping organ.

The front of the head is gently rounded in the female (see however p. 5) whereas in the male it is rather angular and has a slight projection like a chitinous blister on the dorsal side (Fig. 25*b*). The rostral filaments are long and slender and just anterior to their roots, on the ventral side of the head, there is a pair of very small hair-like structures, the frontal organs (Fig. 5) which have a group of sensory cells at their roots. They are easiest to see in a moult or when the animal is lying on its side.

Each of the antennules or first antennae is longer than the body by two or three segments and has 25 segments in the female, the anterior edge being well supplied with short bristles. The penultimate and antepenultimate segments bear long backwardly directed plumose setae which are characteristic of the genus. In the female the two setae are of equal length; in the male the proximal one is longer than the distal. In the male the first two segments of each antennule are fused into a flattened plate and the anterior side carries many sensory aesthetascs. Each of the second antennae (Fig. 3*a*) has a 7-segmented outer and a 2-segmented inner, ramus. The mandible (Fig. 3*b*) is well developed and the mandibular palp biramous, with five segments in the outer and two in the inner ramus. The mandibles lie on either side of the mouth between the anterior labrum and the posterior labium. These latter structures have been described in detail by With (1915).

There has been much discussion about the number of segments and their homology in the three following pairs of appendages. In each appendage there is a protopod formed usually of a precoxa, a coxa and a basipod although it is sometimes 4-segmented.

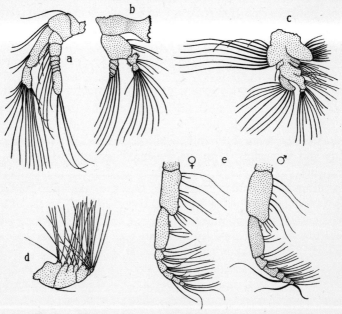

FIG. 3. The mouthparts of adult *Calanus finmarchicus*.
(*a*) antenna, (*b*) mandible, (*c*) maxillule, (*d*) maxilla, (*e*) maxillipede, male and female.

The maxillule (Fig. 3*c*) is a complicated structure having on its protopod, both internally and externally, a series of lobes bearing setae. According to Gurney (1931) the protopod is 4-segmented. The precoxa carries a gnathobase with short stout bristles, the coxa carries the epipod and the first internal lobe, the first basipod carries the second internal lobe and the small external lobe with one seta, and the fourth segment carries the exopod and endopod. The functional joint occurs between the second and third segments. Giesbrecht (1892), Sars (1903) and Borradaile (1926) differ from Gurney in their interpretation of this limb.

The maxilla and the maxillipede are set very close to one another and were at first thought to be derived from one limb-bud. It was later discovered that not only did they originate separately but that the maxillipede belonged to the thorax and was homologous with the swimming feet.

The maxilla (Fig. 3d) is uniramous and there are a series of setose endites of which the fifth and sixth are sometimes regarded as belonging to the protopod, sometimes to the endopod. The single external seta has sometimes been considered as a vestigial exopod (see Lang, 1947).

The maxillipede (Fig. 3e) is also a uniramous limb with a three-segmented protopod and a 5- or 6-segmented endopod. The disputed segment is seen as a small lobe bearing two setae on the distal end of the third protopod segment. Gurney says that it is seen in other species, and sometimes even in *Calanus*, to be on a separate segment, and he regards it as the first endopod segment. Sømme (1934) also mentions having found the endopod 6-jointed. The difference between the sexes is shown in the figure.

In life the antennules are usually held out at right angles to the body and are used as supporting organs. The exopods of the antennae curve up closely over the back while the endopods project ventrally. The setae of the latter and of the mandibles and maxillules spread out in a series of fans laterally and ventrally. Those of the maxillae are directed forward. The maxillipedes usually curve out ventrally and anteriorly beyond the other limbs although Lowndes (1935) says that they may also be swung either forward and inwards or backwards and outwards. The use of these limbs in feeding is described on pp. 98-99.

The swimming feet (Fig. 4 a-e) in a healthy *Calanus* are flexed forwards at an angle and the tips of the first reach almost to the mouth.

A chitinous plate, the 'coupler', unites the two limbs of each pair of swimming feet (p. 1 - p. 5) and ensures that they move simultaneously. The first four pairs of swimming feet are alike in both sexes. There is a coxa and a basipod; the first bears a plumose seta in all but p. 5 and the second, in p. 1 only, bears a longer, rather S-shaped, plumose seta. Although shorter than the external ramus the internal ramus is well developed and 3-jointed. The spines at the outer corners of the joints of the external ramus in p. 1 are weak and seta-like, but in the other legs they are stronger and the terminal one in p. 4 and p. 5 is a well developed serrated blade. On the internal ramus the number of setae on the successive segments varies. In $p.$ 1 - $p.$ 4 the first segments bear one each, the second two each, whereas the numbers on the third segments are 6, 8, 8, on $p.$ 1, 2, and 3 respectively. On $p.$ 4 the normal number for the third segment is 7 (Giesbrecht, 1892; Sars, 1903; and present observations) although Wilson (1932) states that it is 5, and Lebour (1916) figures it in Stage V with 8.

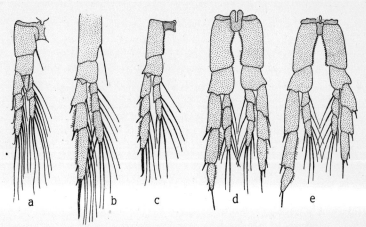

FIG. 4.   The swimming feet of adult *Calanus finmarchicus*
(a) *p*.1, (b) *p*.4, (c) *p*.5, female, (d) *p*.5, male *finmarchicus*, (e) *p*.5, male *helgolandicus*.

The fifth pair of swimming feet (Fig. 4 *c*, *d*) is different in the two sexes. In the adults the number of setae on the successive segments of the internal rami on $p.$ 5 are 1, 1, 5 (1 being external) in the female, and 1, 1, 6 (2 being external) in the male. Giesbrecht mentions that the number is rather variable and Currie (1918) has confirmed this. She says that both in Stage V and in adult females the number of external setae on the terminal segment varies, being sometimes one, sometimes two and occasionally different on the right and left ramus of the same pair. About one quarter of the Stage V examined had only one external seta on each ramus, about one quarter of the females had two, but only a single divergence from the normal two was found among males. The variation in Stage V, however, showed no relation to the sex.

In the male $p.$ 5 (Fig. 4*d*) the inner edge of the coxa is hollowed; the left external ramus bears no setae and is fringed with fine hairs on the inner sides of its last two segments (not on the outer sides as in the female) whereas the last segment is much shorter than in the female and rather pear-shaped. The left external ramus is longer than the right which is fringed (like the female) on the external sides of its second and third segments; these are normal in appearance but carry no setae. The internal rami on both sides are normal, the left only slightly longer than the right and reaching about half-way up the penultimate segment of the external ramus. Both right and left are fringed externally.

As already mentioned (pp. 5-6) the degree of asymmetry is more marked in the *helgolandicus* form (Fig. 4*e*). A single male (*finmarchicus* form) has been seen with a symmetrical pair of fifth legs both of which had the structure of left legs.

With (1915) considers that the cutaneous glands and pores on the swimming feet of copepods are of importance systematically. In *C. finmarchicus* there are none on the first pair except for an occasional small pore on the anterior surface of each of the internal rami at the base of the seta. On *p.* 2-5 he found a minute pore on the anterior surface at the base of a minute seta on each basipod; in the first and second segments of the external ramus of each of the last four pairs of legs, a more or less distinct pore was found at the base of the external seta, and a distinct pore at the bases of the second and third setae respectively of the third segment. In addition to these a pore was found in *p.* 3 and 4, but not often in *p.* 2, in the position of the absent first seta on this third segment.

The penultimate metasome segment in the male has a pair of small setae, and the corners of the last segment in both sexes are bluntly rounded.

The urosome is 5-segmented in the male, but 4-segmented in the female in which the first two have fused. The male genital opening is on the first segment, and is a slit slightly to the left of the middle line; that of the female, opening also upon the first segment, is central, unpaired, and crescent-shaped. Here too are the openings of the paired spermathecal sacs.

The caudal rami are alike in both sexes except that those of the male are articulated to the anal segment and in preserved specimens are often found outspread.

In a vessel containing living *Calanus* the adults are easily distinguishable to the naked eye, the male by the thickened basal part of the antennules and the usually rather greater development of red pigment; the female by its slight opacity and the presence of a white spot (the spermathecal sacs) on the first segment of the urosome.

Internal Anatomy

The internal anatomy of *Calanus* has been described by Lowe (1935) and the short account in this and the following chapter is taken mainly from her paper, to which the reader is referred for further details.

There is an endoskeleton represented firstly by two tendinous ventral endosternites which serve as supports for the muscles of the antennae and mouth parts and secondly by numerous chitinous ingrowths which usually also serve for the attachment of muscles. The first endosternite lies between the bases of the mandibles just behind the oesophagus and is triangular with projections running both forward and backward. It supports the muscles of the antennae, mandibles, and maxillules. The second is more rod shaped, lies at the level of the maxillae and has a pair of lateral projections. It supports muscles for the maxillules, maxillae and maxillipedes. Of the chitinous ingrowths the largest pair rise from the ventral surface behind and lateral to the base of the maxillules and extend dorso-laterally. Other projections extend inwards from the bases of the swimming feet and serve as supports for their flexor muscles. There are also three pairs of very slender chitinous struts projecting in from the ventral surface, passing through the ventral longitudinal muscles and supporting the genital ducts.

The main muscle bands of the metasome are clearly seen in the living animal. A single pair of ventral longitudinal muscles extends from the main pair of chitinous struts described above to the posterior end of the metasome where each is connected by a tendon to the ventral exoskeleton and to the ventral abdominal muscles. The paired dorsal longitudinal muscles lie close to the exoskeleton and each is disposed in seven bands attached anteriorly to the dorsal and lateral exoskeleton at the level of the oesophagus. The most dorsal are attached posteriorly to the anterior border of the second free thoracic segment, the second, third and fourth bands to the anterior borders of the third, fourth, and fifth free segments, the fifth to the posterior border of the fifth free segment and the sixth and seventh to the anterior border of the first urosome segment. There is besides a pair of minute muscles stretching from the dorsal exoskeleton of the sixth thoracic segment to the anterior border of the first urosomal segment. Also conspicuous in the living animal are the bands of muscles which run transversely from the appendages of the head fanning out on the dorsal exoskeleton. These are more prominent in the male than in the female, but they have not been described in detail.

Besides these there are three pairs of slender muscles unconnected with the main set. One pair runs dorsally from the first to the fourth thoracic segment and serves as a support to the heart. The second runs from the dorsal exoskeleton to the pericardial floor and is concerned in the expansion and contraction of the pericardium. The third pair lie in the wall of the genital ducts (both are present in the male even although there is no duct on the right side) and probably support them.

A short oesophagus (Fig. 5) connects the mouth with the main part of the gut. The labrum immediately in front of the mouth forms part of its anterior wall and bears two rows of fine chitinous teeth as well as the eight openings of the labral glands. The oesophagus opens into the mid-gut which is wide in the head region and has a wide diverticulum stretching

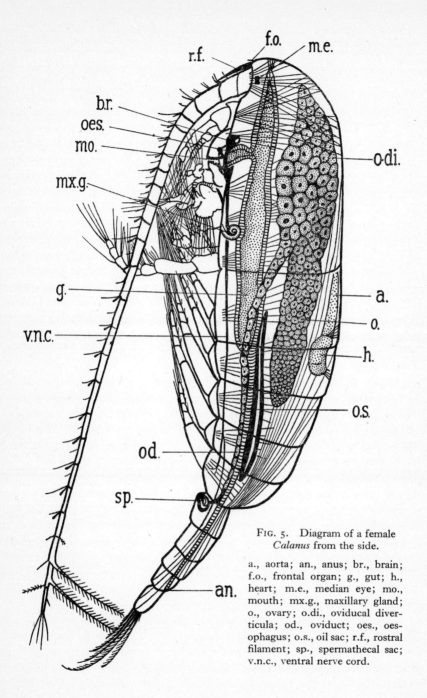

r.f.   f.o.   m.e.

b.r.

oes.

mo.

mx.g.

g.

v.n.c.

od.

sp.

an.

o.di.

a.

o.

h.

o.s.

FIG. 5.   Diagram of a female
Calanus from the side.

a., aorta; an., anus; br., brain;
f.o., frontal organ; g., gut; h.,
heart; m.e., median eye; mo.,
mouth; mx.g., maxillary gland;
o., ovary; o.di., oviducal diverticula; od., oviduct; oes., oesophagus; o.s., oil sac; r.f., rostral
filament; sp., spermathecal sac;
v.n.c., ventral nerve cord.

forward almost to the front end of the head, to which it is attached by a strand of connective tissue. About the level of the second free segment of the thorax the gut suddenly narrows and continues backwards to the proctodaeum, which occupies little more than the last urosome segment. The anus is situated dorsally between the rami of the caudal furcae.

Part of the wide central portion of the gut (but not the diverticulum) is lined by a glandular epithelium. Although Lowe says that this part occupies only the first two thoracic segments, glandular cells may be seen anterior to this. The cells are large and project irregularly into the gut each containing a large vacuole full of secretion. The protoplasm and nucleus are confined to the base of the cell. Interspersed among the glandular cells are narrow granular cells, staining deeply, with median nuclei. Since there are no separate glands the digestive ferments are presumably secreted in this part of the gut. The wide part of the gut including the diverticulum is, in the living animal, in constant movement and any food mass within it is pushed backwards and forwards continuously.

Both in the diverticulum and in the narrow posterior part the gut is lined with cubical non-vacuolated cells.

Although there are no separate glands, there are at the front end of the diverticulum a pair of small pockets which may be vestiges of digestive diverticula such as are found in the Cladocera.

The midgut has a series of striated circular muscles lying outside the epithelium and arranged in bands. They are most strongly developed in the oesophagus. There is also a layer of longitudinal non-striated fibrils inside the circular muscles in some parts of the gut.

There are eight labral glands, four on each side, each with its own opening. Each gland is formed of one multinucleate cell which extends throughout the whole labrum and projects into the body cavity. The duct is hollowed out of the lower part of the syncytium.

One of the most characteristic features of a living *Calanus* is the shining bolster of oil which lies along the middle of the body. The oil is secreted into an elongated sac which reaches from the head to the posterior end of the metasome. Anteriorly it lies above the mid-gut but in the thorax it gradually moves round to the left side displacing the gut as it does so, so that it comes to lie centrally. The anterior part is, in the female, attached to the left oviduct, the central part to the left side of the gut and posteriorly it ends as a cord of cells attached to the left side of the pericardial floor so it is probable that there was once a pair of sacs. Indeed in a number of Lowe's specimens a rudimentary sac was present as a cord of cells attached to the gut.

In the early copepodites, the male, and the immature female, the sac with its contained oil stretches the whole length of the metasome, but as the female matures the sac usually diminishes and in the mature female the anterior end is sometimes reduced to a cord of cells attached to the left oviduct. The space which it previously occupied is filled with the diverticula from the oviducts containing a mass of eggs. In some females

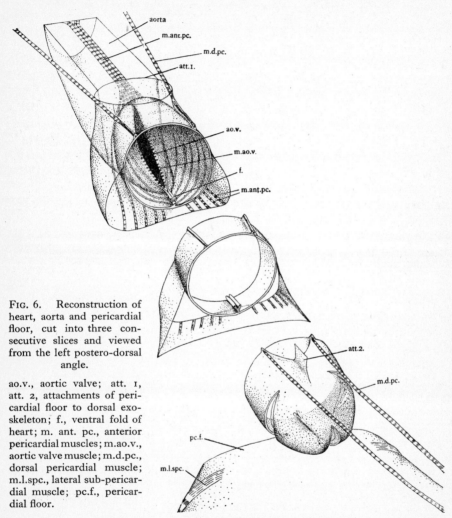

FIG. 6. Reconstruction of heart, aorta and pericardial floor, cut into three consecutive slices and viewed from the left postero-dorsal angle.

ao.v., aortic valve; att. 1, att. 2, attachments of pericardial floor to dorsal exoskeleton; f., ventral fold of heart; m. ant. pc., anterior pericardial muscles; m.ao.v., aortic valve muscle; m.d.pc., dorsal pericardial muscle; m.l.spc., lateral sub-pericardial muscle; pc.f., pericardial floor.

however, particularly in summer when food is plentiful, the oil extends to the head end even when the diverticula are full of large eggs. The size of the sac varies greatly from one *Calanus* to another and is largest in Stage V. Even weeks of starvation do not cause it to disappear entirely and the Stage V *Calanus* found in January, which have survived since the previous autumn, often possess large sacs filled with oil. Lowe refers to the sac as a 'hydrostatic' organ but there is no evidence that it can be used as such to control the depth at which the *Calanus* swims. Its size seems rather to depend on the presence of abundant food in the water.

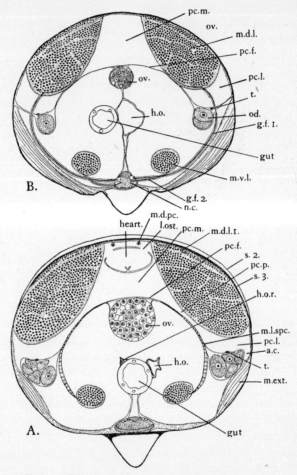

FIG. 7.   Diagrammatic transverse slices of the thorax.

(A) at junction of second and third thoracic segments; (B) at junction of third and fourth thoracic segments.

g.f.1, g.f.2, giant fibres; h.o., oilsac; h.o.r., rudimentary right oilsac; l.ost., lateral ostium; m.d.l., dorsal longitudinal muscles; m.d.l.1, posterior attachment of first dorsal longi-tudinal muscle to exoskeleton; m.d.pc., dorsal pericardial muscle; m.ext., extensor muscle of swimming foot; m.l.spc., lateral sub-pericardial muscle; m.v.l., ventral longi-tudinal muscle; n.c., nerve cord; od., oviduct; ov., ovary; pc.f., pericardial floor; pc.l., lateral pericardial cavity; pc.m., median pericardial cavity; pc.p., pericardial passage; s.2, s.3, terga of second and third thoracic segments; t., tendon of muscle attached to genital duct.

The excretory system consists of a pair of maxillary glands. Each is composed of an end sac, opening by a narrow orifice surrounded by three guard cells into the swollen end of the duct. The duct makes a single coil and opens in a depression on the inner side of the basal joint of the maxilla. The end sac is pentagonal, its wall consists of vacuolated cells with indistinct outlines and it is almost surrounded by the lateral blood sinus. The antennal gland described by Grobben (1881) in the nauplius has disappeared in the adult (see p. 47).

The heart (Figs. 5 and 6) is a small ovoid body lying dorsally beneath the junction of the second and third thoracic segments. It has four openings, one, at the front end ventrally, opening into the aorta and provided with valves. The other three are venous ostia; two are situated laterally, in the posterior half of the heart, the third is ventral, at the posterior end. The complicated musculature of the heart has been fully described by Lowe; it is enough to say here that when the muscles of the heart itself, both circular and longitudinal, contract, the aortic valve opens and the ostia (which also possess valves) close. The muscles surrounding the aortic valve belong essentially to the pericardial floor and when these contract, the aortic opening is closed.

The pericardium forms the dorsal part of the body cavity in the five free thoracic segments. At the anterior end the dorsal part of the pericardial membrane is wrapped round the heart and partly fused with it; posteriorly it forms a sling attaching the heart to the dorsal body wall. Figs. 7A and B show the relations of the ventral part of the pericardium to the dorsal longitudinal muscles, the oviducts and the body wall.

The pericardial floor is raised and depressed synchronously with the beating of the heart. When the floor is depressed the heart is in systole; when it is raised, in diastole. The aortic valve is closed in diastole and blood from the pericardium enters and fills the heart. When the pericardial floor is depressed, the heart contracts pushing the blood into the aorta through the now open aortic valve, and blood is drawn into the pericardium from the perivisceral space. There are no muscles in the aorta, which runs forward to the front end of the head, but the blood is probably driven along by the force of the heart and thence by a pair of dorso-ventral sinuses into the spaces round the brain and into another main sinus, the supraneural. This runs above the nerve cord in the head end, splits to go round the oesophagus and the endosternites and finally, in the second thoracic segment, opens into the main perivisceral cavity. Numerous smaller sinuses supply the labrum, the mouth parts and the swimming feet. Blood is returned from the perivisceral cavity into the pericardium by a series of paired dorso-ventral canals running between the muscles just under the exoskeleton. Some of the muscles associated with the mouth parts may, by their movements, help in the circulation of the blood although not directly concerned with it.

The reproductive system is described in Chapter III.

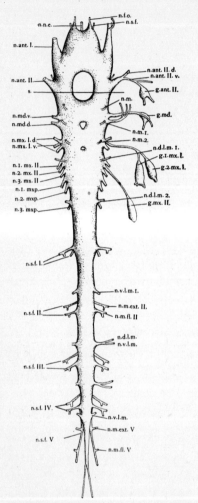

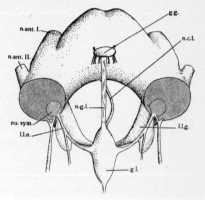

FIG. 9. Posterior aspect of brain showing sympathetic system; the para-oesophageal cords are cut through along the line 's' in Fig. 8.

g.ant.II, basal ganglion of antennal nerve; g.g., gastric ganglion; g.l., labral ganglion; g.md., basal ganglion of the mandibular nerve; g.1 and 2 mx. I, basal ganglia of maxillulary nerve; g.mx.II, basal ganglion of the maxillary nerve; l.l.g., and l.l.n., labral loop of ganglion cells; n.ant.I, antennular nerve; n.ant.II, antennal nerve; n.ant.II d. and v., dorsal and ventral roots of the antennal nerve; n.c.l., nerve connecting labral ganglion with brain; n.d.l.m., n.d.l.m.I and II, nerves (giant fibre) supplying dorsal longitudinal muscles; n.f.o., and n.s.f., nerves to frontal organ; n.g.l., nerve connecting labral and gastric ganglia; n.l.l., nerve supplying labrum; n.m., n.m. 1 and 2, nerves supplying muscles from the endosternite to the antenna, mandible and maxillule; n.m.ext. II and V, nerves to extensor muscles of *p*.II and V; n.m.fl. II and V, nerves to flexor muscles of *p*. II and V; n.md.v. and d., ventral and dorsal roots of mandibular nerve; n.mx. I v. and d., ventral and dorsal roots of maxillulary nerve; n.1-3 mx. II, maxillary nerves; n.1-3 mxp., maxillipedal nerves; n.n.e., nerve to nauplius eye; n.s.f. I to V, nerves to the five pairs of swimming feet; nu.sym., sympathetic nucleus; n.v.l.m., n.v.l.m.1., nerves to ventral longitudinal muscles.

FIG. 8. Dorsal aspect of central nervous system, showing basal ganglia and roots of nerves.

The central nervous system consists of the cerebral lobes or brain and the ventral nerve cord (Figs. 8 and 9). The brain forms the most massive part, lying in front of the oesophagus and splitting into two loops round it which unite behind to form the single ventral nerve cord (Fig. 5). This is oval in section and passes down the whole length of the body, dividing in the last metasome segment into dorsal and ventral branches. The two halves of the cord are completely fused except for two small splits where muscles pass through from the endosternite to the body wall.

From the front end of the brain nerves run to the eye and frontal organs. The eye is a simple reddish pigment spot with a lens-like mass on either side; the external part of the frontal organs have already been mentioned (p. 11). Besides the sensory cells at the root of each hair there is a lateral glandular portion which is separately innervated and which perhaps corresponds to the lateral frontal organs of Cladocera. The function of the frontal organ is unknown. In the front end of the brain is a pair of small statocysts each consisting of a spherical cavity containing a single concretion. Their innervation has not been observed.

Nerves are given off to the appendages either from the brain, the oesophageal loops or the ventral nerve cord. Most of these nerves consist of a dorsal and a ventral root, sometimes coming off together and sometimes separately. In most the ventral root is the sensory and the dorsal the motor nerve but in those to the antennules the position is reversed and the ventral root contains mainly giant motor fibres. Where in the last thoracic segment the cord divides, the dorsal branch subdivides soon after into two nerves which run down the urosome and end one in each caudal ramus, while the ventral branch supplies the fifth pair of swimming feet and their muscles. Besides the nerves to the appendages there is a series of intersegmental nerves composed of giant fibres supplying the longitudinal trunk muscles.

The sympathetic nervous system is represented by three ganglia. The first and largest, the labral ganglion, lies below the cerebral lobes and has nervous connections to the cerebral lobes, to the circum-oesophageal loops and to the junction of these behind the oesophagus. The second, the gastric ganglion lies in the angle between the oesophagus and the mid-gut diverticulum and has connections to the cerebral lobes and the labral ganglion. It also sends nerves to the mid-gut. The third ganglion lies on the dorsal wall of the anterior end of the mid-gut diverticulum. It gives off a nerve to the wall of the aorta and is probably connected with the gastric ganglion.

Lowe describes in detail the complicated internal structure of the brain and cord with its nerve centres and fibre tracts.

Calanus also possesses a well developed system of giant nerve fibres. The main part of the system is a prominent pair of fibres which originates in the brain, one on each side near the antennular motor nucleus, perhaps in a single giant cell. Each sends off a nerve to an antennular muscle, then crosses to the opposite side and runs down on the inside of the oesophageal loops. In the ventral cord they run dorso-laterally along the whole length near the surface, each giving off in its course eight branches. The first pair leaves the cord at the level of the maxillary nerve and runs to the dorsal longitudinal trunk muscles; the second leaves above the third maxillipedal nerve and takes a similar course. Behind the first thoracic segment the main giant fibres on each side give off branches alternately to the segmental and intersegmental nerves of the thoracic segments. The segmental branches supply the flexor muscles of the swimming feet and the intersegmental branches supply the dorsal longitudinal trunk muscles. The main giant fibres pass out of the cord into the flexor muscles of the fourth feet. The fifth feet flexor muscles are also innervated by a giant fibre but a connection between this and the main giant fibre was not traced. Although in most copepods the fifth pair of swimming feet are used more for reproduction than for swimming, in *Calanus* they resemble closely the first four pairs and it is curious that the innervation should be so different.

Apart from the main giant fibres there are others which, although conspicuous by their size, are not connected with the main system and are distributed like ordinary motor fibres.

All the giant fibres whose origin was traced were found to rise from giant cells in the brain and nerve cord and to end in the muscles as a number of thin tapering branches.

It will be seen that the main giant fibre system supplies all the muscles of *Calanus* which are used in its rapid leaping escape movements, namely those in the antennules, four of the five pairs of swimming feet, and the dorsal longitudinal muscles. When all the trunk muscles contract the thorax is shortened and the abdomen is pulled towards the contracting side thus acting as a rudder. Lowe suggests that the whole system forms a great reflex arc, the effector part of it represented by the muscles mentioned above. The receptor part is not so clearly defined but since the main fibres form a chiasma in the brain, the receptors are probably paired. Neither the frontal organs nor the eye seem likely to function thus and it is probably the antennules which are responsible. They have sensory hairs along their whole length and are held extended during swimming. The fact that all the muscles responsible are innervated by branches of the same giant nerve must make for efficiency and rapidity in the escape movement.

CHAPTER III

REPRODUCTION

In both sexes there is a single median gonad attached to the pericardial floor and bulging into the perivisceral cavity. The male has one and the female two ducts connecting the gonad to the single genital opening on the first urosome segment.

Male

In the male the genital duct rises from the anterior end of the testis and passes back on the left side, opening to the exterior in the first abdominal segment by a wide ventro-lateral slit in its left posterior border. Although a right duct is never functional, it is represented by an unattached cord of cells lying in the right side of the pericardial floor.

Heberer (1924, 1932*a* and *b*, 1937) has made a detailed study of the genital system of male copepods including that of *Calanus* which he considers as the basic type. He divides the genital tract into six sections consisting of the testis and five differentiated tracts of duct, the *vas deferens*, seminal vesicle, 'former', spermatophore sac, and *ductus ejaculatorius*. Most of these can be seen easily in the living *Calanus*.

According to Lowe (1935) the testis is a pear-shaped body lying dorsally in the first free thoracic somite but this is an early stage and observations at Millport on a large number of males show that it is usually more fully developed and is seen as a cylindrical body extending into the third or even the fourth free thoracic somite. The *vas deferens* is a thick-walled glandular tube rising from the anterior end of the testis and running first ventrally and then posteriorly with

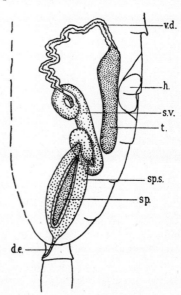

FIG. 10. Genital system of male seen from left side.

d.e., ductus ejaculatorius; h., heart; sp., spermatophore; sp.s., spermatophore sac; s.v., seminal vesicle; t., testis; v.d., vas deferens.

many twists and turns; its narrow lumen contains a strand of sperm and secretion. The seminal vesicle is a thin-walled coiled tube filled with a thick mass of sperm and secretion; the degree of coiling varies from one male to another and may depend on the state of maturity. As a rule it is shaped like a compressed C with the ends often showing a further small turn. There is always a sharp bend between seminal vesicle and sper- matophore sac and usually another between seminal vesicle and *vas deferens* but in the simpler forms there may be only a U-shaped bend at the posterior end. Fig. 10 shows the most usual arrangement. The sper- matophore sac is thick-walled and glandular and usually contains a spermatophore; its cavity is often filled with a mass of secretion. The junction of the seminal vesicle with the spermatophore sac, i.e. the 'former' according to Heberer, is difficult to see since the anterior end of the second is embraced by a loop of the first. The short muscular *ductus ejaculatorius* leads from the spermatophore sac to the genital opening.

During the early development of the genital cells, according to Heberer, and especially in Stage V, there is a considerable production of nucleolar material by the nucleus and this passes first into the cytoplasm and finally into the body fluid. Heberer suggests that it may consist of hormone-like substances and may influence the development of the secondary sexual characters.

The testis can be divided into three zones, a multiplication zone at the hind end, a zone in the middle where the spermatocyte divisions are going on and a zone of spermatozoa in front. The last is partly surrounded by the second and forms a mass round the opening of the *vas deferens*.

The chromosomes have been studied by Heberer (1924, 1932a) and recently by Dr J. P. Harding (personal communication). Most of the Calanoida have a haploid number of 16 or 17 and according to Harding the number in both *Calanus finmarchicus* and *C. helgolandicus* is 17. They tend to be rather crowded together in spermatogenesis so that they are not easy to study individually in the testis. In the male, the chromosomes are elongated and most of them are paired end to end with only one or two of the bivalent forming rings. This is in marked contrast to the con- dition in the female where all, or nearly all, the bivalents form rings. Occasionally a polar view of a plate has the contracted chromosomes well enough separated for them to be counted. Heberer has seen small uni- valent chromosomes in Centropagids and considers them as sex chromo- somes, the male being the heterogametic sex. He once saw a small chromosome attached to one of the normal in *Calanus* and if this is the sex chromosome, its attachment explains why it has so seldom been seen. Harding also has observed that one of the smallest V-shaped chromosomes is, in one sex, paired with a small J-shaped chromosome.

The completed spermatozoon according to Heberer is an oval and slightly hollowed body about $5\,\mu$ in length, with a rim of cytoplasm and a vacuole at each end (Fig. 11). Lowe states that they are spindle-shaped when ripe but Heberer says that in the spermatophore, owing to pressure, they assume a polygonal shape. When dissected out of either the spermatophore or the spermathecal sacs of the female we have found them of the oval shape figured.

FIG. 11. Spermatozoa (about 5μ) of *Calanus finmarchicus* (after Heberer).

According to Heberer the wall of the *vas deferens* (Fig. 10) is composed of cells which have several nuclei and are highly secretory and it can be divided functionally into two parts. The proximal part secretes a substance which forms the core of the spermatophore and the distal part secretes the spermatophore wall. The seminal vesicle is lined with flat syncytial cells and has no secretory function. It acts as a storage space for masses of sperm and secretion and, according to Lowe, it is here that these take up their final positions, the sperm forming a peripheral layer on a central core of secretion.

A muscular sphincter separates the seminal vesicle from the spermatophore sac (Heberer, 1932*b*) and the latter is differentiated into two parts, the 'former' and the sac proper. In the 'former' the spermatophore is shaped and a sticky substance is secreted which during copulation helps to attach it to the female genital segment. The walls of the spermatophore sac itself are thick and glandular. In many copepods the sac is visibly differentiated into two regions; in *Calanus* this is not so, but, as in other copepods, two distinct secretions are produced.

Not all the spermatozoa in the spermatophore are used for fertilization. In the proximal part of the spermatophore sac the secretion produced increases the resistance of the sperm to swelling; the secretion of the distal part has an opposite effect and promotes swelling. After extrusion and attachment to the female therefore the sperm at the distal end swell up and push out the remaining contents of the spermatophore, i.e. the functional sperm. The core substance, which by contact with sea water gels as it is extruded, forms a channel through which the sperm are pushed into the spermathecal sacs of the female. In ripe males spermatophores can easily be squeezed out and Heberer found repeatedly that if one was removed before the distal secretion had been added no spermatozoa swelled up. The spermatophore sac secretions must presumably pass through the thin wall ($2\text{-}3\,\mu$ thick) of the spermatophore.

The spermatophore is an elongated sac, over $400\,\mu$ long without the neck and about 80 μ wide. After extrusion the two functionally different halves of the spermatophore contents can be distinguished by a difference in their refractive index.

Heberer's account differs in some ways from that given by Lowe (1935). She says that globules of eosinophil substance are produced in the testis and pass down the *vas deferens* into the seminal vesicle to form the core of the spermatophore. She suggests that since the seminal vesicle wall is not secretory, the wall of the spermatophore must be secreted in the spermatophore sac and then passed back into the seminal vesicle. The whole mass of core, sperm and wall is then passed in sections back into the spermatophore sac, the bend in the duct between them remaining empty in the meantime. In the sac the lower part of the spermatophore is given shape, although the upper part is incomplete and the long tubular neck is formed when the spermatophore is extruded.

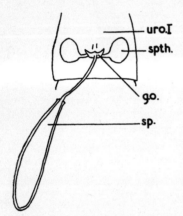

Fig. 12. Ventral aspect of first urosome segment of female showing spermatophore attached to genital aperture.

uro. I., first urosome segment; spth., spermatheca; g.o., genital opening; sp., spermatophore (after Lowe).

Further investigation is obviously needed to determine the nature, place of formation and method of entry of the various components of the spermatophore.

Little is known about the rate of formation of spermatophores or how many one male can produce during its lifetime. Males moulted from Stage V in the laboratory at Millport in June had formed spermatophores in the spermatophore sac within a fortnight. Copulation has not been observed in *Calanus*. Rose (1933) states that the male is not very efficient in transferring the spermatophore and that it is quite frequently found attached elsewhere than to the genital segment. In our specimens such abnormal deposition has rarely been found and practically all females carrying spermatophores were normally fertilized and bore one only, attached to the genital segment (Figs. 12 and 13a). Occasionally, however, a female is found carrying more than one but rarely more than two or three. Gibbons (1936) has reported a female with 15. It is unusual to find spermatophores attached to any stage but the adult female but Marshall, Nicholls and Orr (1934) described a Stage V with 13 attached not only to the first urosome segment but elsewhere on the urosome and even on the swimming legs. In cases of abnormal deposition the neck of the spermatophore may be much longer than usual, may be twisted round

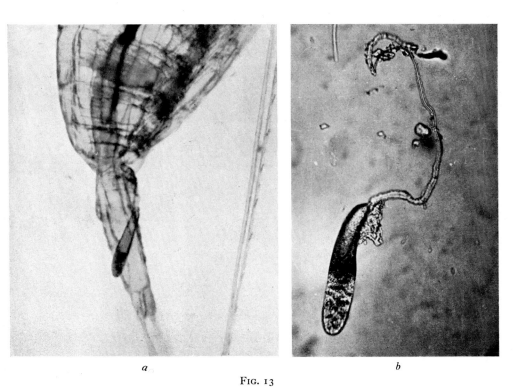

a   b

Fig. 13

(*a*) photograph of spermatophore attached to female, (*b*) ($\times$90) spermatophore which was attached to a Stage V, and so has an exceptionally long neck, and is undischarged.

the feet or abdomen and may still be apparently full of sperm (Fig. 13*b*). Gibbons has made the ingenious suggestion that in these cases the male has for some reason been unable to detach itself and that 15 represents the total production of one male. Unfortunately male development does not seem to go on so smoothly in the laboratory as does that of the female, and in spite of keeping late Stage V and newly-moulted or unfertilized females along with males for some weeks, no attachment of spermatophores could be found.

In plankton catches females usually out-number males greatly and although this (see pp. 79-80) is partly because of the shorter life of the males, and partly because their maximum number occurs earlier in the breeding cycle than that of the females, it still remains a problem how all the females, especially those moulting late, can be fertilized. That very few females remain unfertilized is obvious from an examination of the spermathecal sacs which are almost always dark and full. The majority of the males moult first and presumably, like the females, take some time to ripen the genital products. When after a week or two the majority of females moult, the males will be ready to fertilize them, for we know that fertilization usually occurs at an early stage in the development of the female gonad and that the spermatophore is retained only for a short time.

In 1933 in Loch Striven it was found that of 674 females with ovaries in an early or medium state 17·4% carried spermatophores whereas of 1474 ripe females less than 1% did so. When brought into the laboratory, females with spermatophores never retained them for more than two days and they were usually lost within 24 hours. It is rare to find more than a small percentage of the females carrying them but on one occasion (9th April 1951) the majority of females were in the medium state and had spermatophores attached.

Female

In the female in the earliest stages the gonad is triangular or pear-shaped but as it develops the middle part becomes a long cylinder. As a rule the newly moulted female has a small ovary but this is not invariable and a Stage V can moult into a female which may be in any state between immaturity and ripeness (see p. 34). The state of development depends very largely, if not entirely, on the amount of food present.

Two oviducts rise from the anterior end of the ovary (Fig. 5) and cross the body in a posterior and ventral direction; they then run ventral to and parallel to the gut, which often obscures them. As the female matures two diverticula develop from the front ends of the oviducts and run forward into the head region. Each diverticulum is divided into an upper and lower channel by a membranous partition which probably represents the fused adjacent walls of a U-shaped loop. When ripe the posterior parts of the oviducts are produced into short diverticula but these are probably only temporary extensions caused by the enlarging eggs. The oocytes from the ovary pass forward into the upper channels and then back along the ventral channels and into the oviducts proper. As the ducts enter the abdomen they approach one another, joining as they reach the genital opening. A pair of small oval spermathecae are present at the sides of the genital opening and are connected to it by a pair of short canals. These and the spermathecae are lined with chitin. The oviducts open by a short median chitinized portion into a small cavity formed by the union of the spermathecal ducts. The genital opening is crescentic in shape with the horns of the crescent extending forward as grooves in the chitin (Fig. 12).

Hilton (1931) has described oogenesis in detail and Dr Harding has studied the chromosomes of the maturation divisions and early cleavage stages.

According to Hilton the ovary can be divided into three zones; the first of these, at the posterior tip of the ovary, is the multiplication zone; the second, anterior to it, is the synapsis zone and contains oocytes in the early stages of the maturation divisions; the third is the growth zone, and the oocyte passes through its entire growth period before maturation is completed.

The nucleus of the oogonial cell contains two or three nucleoli, one of which is a plasmosome and is larger than the rest. The smaller nucleoli are karyosomes. The final oogonial mitoses take place in the region just behind the synapsis zone. The nucleoli disappear before the breakdown of the nuclear membrane and eventually 34 chromosomes appear. The other stages of division are passed through rapidly and after a short resting stage the nucleolus re-forms and the first maturation division begins. It is in this stage that the oocyte undergoes the whole of its growth, passing in the course of it into the oviducal diverticula and thence down the oviducts. However we have noticed that there are small eggs visible in the posterior part of the oviduct in the immature state and these must develop in situ. During growth a large amount of nucleolar material is extruded into the cytoplasm and the yolk is also laid down then. The period of most rapid yolk formation seems to be that immediately preceding the breaking down of the nuclear membrane in the ripe oocyte before the first maturation division.

Dr Harding finds that in females which are on the point of laying, the nucleolus is still present and before its disappearance just before the eggs are laid the chromosomes can be seen as single entities. The chromosomes, which are at first thrown into irregular loops, contract, and shortly before

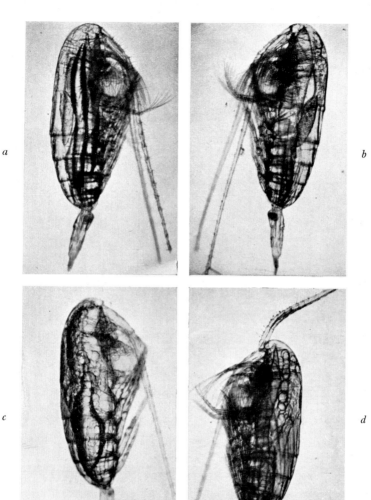

FIG. 14. Female *Calanus* with ovaries in different stages of ripeness.
(*a*) immature, (*b*) medium, (*c*) ripe, (*d*) ripe, showing a single row of
large eggs, the female having already laid many.

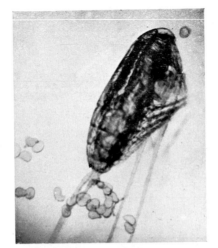

a

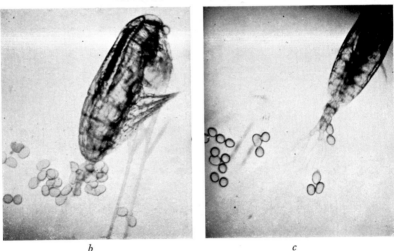

b

c

FIG. 15.   Successive stages in egg laying by a *Calanus*.
(*a*) and (*b*) are of the same ♀, (*b*) a few minutes later than (*a*); some of the same
groups of eggs can be recognized; (*c*) is another ♀ to show the rounding off of the
eggs.

the eggs are laid the 17 bivalents come to lie as compact rings on the equatorial plate.

Hilton states that polar bodies may be observed in the oviduct, flattened against the surface of the egg by its walls. Damas (1905) also says that when polar bodies are seen in the oviducts it is a sign that the females are ripe. Grobben (1881) however states that two are produced, one shortly after the egg is laid and one still later (see p. 43). Dr Harding also finds that the maturation divisions are usually completed after the egg has been laid. If eggs are fixed immediately after being laid the bivalents are usually arranged on the first metaphase plate as just described.

The living female is transparent enough for the state of maturity to be seen under the binocular microscope and five stages have been defined (Marshall and Orr, 1952). In the first or immature state (Fig. 14a) the ovary is small, the diverticula in the head end are just beginning to develop and there is only one row of small eggs to be seen in each of the narrow oviducts as they run across the body. In the second or medium state (Fig. 14b) the ovary is enlarging, the dorsal channels of the diverticula in the head end are full of medium-sized eggs and there may be more than one row of eggs in the oviducts. Both channels of the diverticula fill up in the third state and the eggs in the ventral channel are larger than the rest. This may be called the semi-ripe state. In the fourth state (Fig. 14c and d) the female is ripe and contains a row of eggs in each ventral channel larger than before and there are large eggs forming pouches in the oviducts. In the fifth or spent state the ovary is degenerating and the diverticula and oviducts difficult to see. This state is seen more rarely than any of the others.

A number of females are to be found in which the reproductive organs are in the same state as in the ordinary Stage V. Occasionally Stage V may be seen with a large ovary and well developed diverticula, but as a rule the gonad is very small, no diverticula are visible and the genital ducts are thin cords with no eggs visible in them. Some of these very immature females may be newly-moulted but this category also contains the infertile, the parasitized and the abnormal. They are often characterized by an unusually marked development of red pigment at the hind end of the metasome. Thirty eight such females were kept and fed to see if they would produce eggs, but most of them died without doing so. In some the ovaries became obviously abnormal and in two a nematode became visible in the body cavity after a few days. Twelve reached maturity and laid eggs after from seven to twenty days.

Some time before egg-laying, usually only an hour or two, the large eggs in the ripe female turn slightly pink. Just before laying the colour deepens and the nucleus disappears from view. The eggs are then squeezed out of the narrow genital opening, presumably being fertilized on the way, and emerge as roughly pear-shaped masses adhering to one another (Fig. 15a-c). Sometimes the eggs come from one oviduct only, sometimes from both. When both oviducts are releasing eggs, these squeeze out of the genital opening together and remain attached till they round off; this is why, in a mass of newly-laid eggs, they are often seen lying in pairs. When laying stops, or perhaps only when it is interrupted, the eggs can be seen withdrawing up the oviducts from the abdomen into the meta-some. In a few minutes after laying the eggs separate and round off; they retain a faint pinkish colour for some hours. In many batches of eggs there are several which are mis-shapen or opaque. These die and it is probable that they have not been fertilized. Others appear to be laid with a defective membrane and at a touch disintegrate into a viscid drop of protoplasm.

Occasionally there is formed an abnormally large egg but this, although it may continue to live and develop for over 24 hours has rarely been seen to hatch and form a nauplius. Dr Harding has found triploid embryos and it seems probable that the large eggs are of this type. Indeed one such large egg was fixed shortly after being laid and was found to be a triploid. It seemed possible that *Calanus* might produce parthenogenetic eggs and a number of Stage V were therefore kept to see if the resulting females would lay eggs which could develop. The 22 females thus obtained laid a total of 746 eggs (much fewer than normal) but none of them developed. The great majority went opaque soon after being laid or collapsed when touched, but a few lived for some hours; none survived for as much as 48 hours.

It has been supposed that after the eggs are laid they increase greatly in volume, but if there is any increase it is very small.

After a *Calanus* lays eggs (which may number up to 150 in 24 hours, but is usually 20 to 60), the reproductive organs revert to the 'semi-ripe' state and another batch is ripened. The total egg production has been estimated by keeping in the laboratory a number of females which had been found with spermatophores (and so were presumably recently fer-tilized), feeding them well, and counting the eggs produced (Fig. 16). There was usually a period of up to two weeks before laying began, although three of the females laid at once, indicating either that copulation had taken place later than usual or that the Stage V had been ripe when they moulted. The total production varied considerably but in those which completed their laying was usually about 200-300 eggs. Two however laid considerably more and the most prolific reached a figure of 586 eggs in 74 days. It was observed that towards the end of the egg-laying period the eggs produced were less healthy. Fewer hatched into nauplii and many went opaque at once or were laid with defective membranes. This may indicate that the supply of viable sperm was running out although the number of sperm in the sac is far greater than this and one copulation is usually enough to fertilize the whole egg production of a female.

Egg production often takes place in a series of bursts, each lasting about a week. These bursts tend to recur at intervals of about two weeks but they do not seem to be related to the phases of the moon.

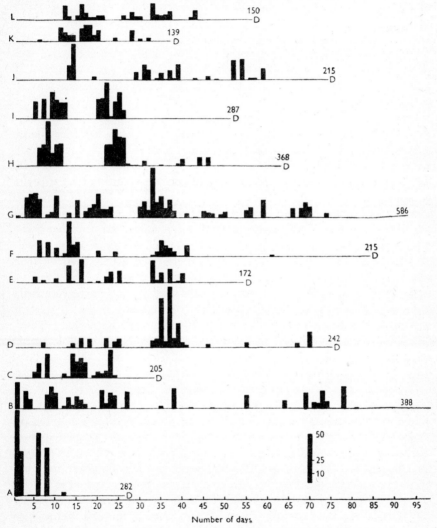

FIG. 16.   Total number of eggs laid by individual *Calanus*.

(A) 5.v.50, (B) 13.vi.50, (C-F) 15.vi.50, (G) 16.vi.50, (H, I) 27.vi.50, (J) 7.vii.50, (K, L) 26.vii.50

REPRODUCTION
EFFECT OF FOOD ON EGG LAYING

Although in the sea in spring (p. 79) there is usually a period of about a month between the moult into female and the start of egg laying, yet the time may be very much shorter. In *Calanus* well fed on *Chlamydomonas*** culture, newly fertilized females, as described above, usually took one or two weeks.

In the *Calanus* kept to find out if virgin females could lay parthenogenetic eggs, the state of maturity was examined frequently. They were kept in 250 ml of sea water changed daily and at the time (May 1951) there were abundant diatoms present, mainly *Skeletonema* and *Thalassiosira*. Of the 36 Stage V, 9 moulted to males and 22 to females. Of the newly-moulted females 3 were in the immature state, 14 in the medium state, 4 were semi-ripe and 1 ripe. The ripe female laid eggs in 6 days and of the semi-ripe, 1 laid in 2 days, 2 in 3 days and 1 in 4 days. The medium and immature became ripe and laid in 3-11 days. Although none of these females was fertilized by a male it does not seem probable that this had any effect on their ripening. It does indicate how greatly feeding can affect the speed of maturing. In some of the Stage V the ovary had begun to enlarge before moult and the diverticula were visible in the head region.

When females in different states of maturity are taken from the sea and their egg production compared in fed and in starved conditions, it is found that fed *Calanus* mature more quickly and lay more eggs than do starved (Marshall and Orr, 1952). In a typical experiment lasting from 9th-16th February, the egg production of 20 immature *Calanus* when fed was 17, 0, 0, 69, 144, 141, 179 on successive days, whereas 20 starved produced no eggs over the same period. The one which laid on the first day was probably wrongly diagnosed as immature. Medium-state and semi-ripe *Calanus* observed at the same time probably included quite a range of degrees of ripeness. Usually one or two laid eggs on the first day, and the number of eggs and of laying females increased from then on. In a typical experiment lasting for 7 days the egg-production by 20 fed *Calanus* on successive days was 26, 72, 149, 193, 178, 155 and 66, a total of 839. In 20 starved at the same time it was 26, 17, 2, 19, 13, 1, 14, a total of 92.

Calanus will remain alive and healthy for weeks when kept singly in glass dishes holding about 25 ml in which the water is changed every other day. They can thus be fed easily with a variety of cultures or can be starved by keeping them in water passed through a membrane filter. It has in this way been possible to test the effect of feeding with a number of different organisms.

*This flagellate, which is Dr Parkes Plymouth strain No. 81 is now indentified as *Dunaliella*.

Fig. 17 shows the results of a feeding experiment in which a number of ripe female *Calanus* were divided into two lots; one lot was fed on a culture of *Chlamydomonas* and one was starved. After the experiment had lasted for 15 days half the starved *Calanus* were fed. The first day's results have been ignored in Fig. 17, because all *Calanus* normally lay eggs the first night after having been brought into the laboratory. The reason why they do so is unknown but apparently something in the shock of capture or examination stimulates a ripe female to lay, whether or not food is present in the water. After the first two days egg production was always greater

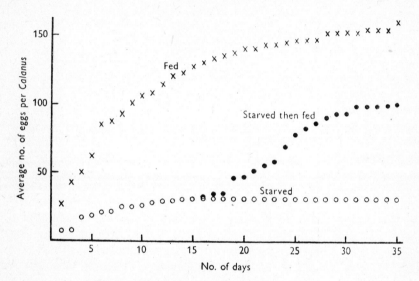

FIG. 17.   Egg laying in starved and fed *Calanus*.

in the fed than in the starved and indeed after a week few of the starved were laying at all. When half of these starved *Calanus* were fed, however, egg laying began again almost at once and their total egg production was about two thirds of that of the females fed all the time. The average total number of eggs per fed *Calanus* (ignoring the first day) was 160 and in those starved and then fed 100, of which 69 were laid after they were fed. Those starved all the time produced an average of 31 of which only a single egg was laid after the fifteenth day.

This experiment was made with females which may or may not have laid before they were caught. One or two indeed which did not lay during the experiment may already have completed their egg laying and this may account for the smaller total numbers laid when compared with the females of Fig. 16.

One interesting fact is that even the starved *Calanus* retained fat up till the end of the experiment. Female *Calanus* as a rule carry less fat than Stage V in the sac which lies along the gut (see p. 18), that in the anterior part usually disappearing gradually as the eggs develop. When mature, however, and under starvation conditions, the fat evidently does not go towards making more eggs but is retained by the animal.

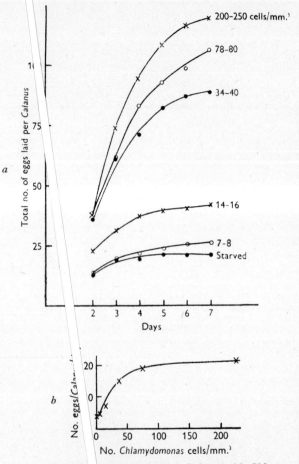

FIG. 18. Experiment on feeding *Calanus* with *Chlamy-domonas* cultures of different concentrations. (*a*) effect on egg production, (*b*) average number of eggs laid per day.

It seems as if females, though ready to lay eggs, do not necessarily do so but may hold them up until conditions are favourable. If this is so, it may explain why in the sea egg production in *Calanus* often seems to coincide with diatom increases.

TABLE I

COMPARISON OF THE EFFECT OF DIFFERENT FOODS ON EGG PRODUCTION

Date begun	No. of Calanus	Food	Total No. of eggs laid on day							Omitting first day			
			1	2	3	4	5	6	7	No. laying	Total No. of eggs	Eggs per batch*	Eggs per Calanus per day
29. i. 51	11	Chlamydomonas	49	28	140	76	157	—	—	9	401	20.4	9.1
	8	Starved	146	4	0	17	9	—	—	3	30	12.5	0.9
21. ii. 51	20	Chlamydomonas	245	66	189	203	304	77	—	18	839	21.4	8.8
	20	Starved	266	32	17	15	0	0	—	6	64	12.4	0.8
27. ii. 51	15	Chlamydomonas	312	174	375	214	177	105	138	14	1183	23.0	15.4
	15	Coscinodiscus	258	17	74	35	26	53	56	13	261	11.5	3.0
	15	Skeletonema	217	142	177	97	231	113	27	14	787	19.5	9.4
	15	Starved	236	32	3	0	11	31	7	9	84	8.9	1.0
6. iii. 51	15	Chlamydomonas	169†	406	358	230	70	82	—	14	1146	29.0	16.4
	15	Peridinium	331†	132	313	86	213	111	—	15	865	24.8	11.5
	15	Rhizosolenia	514	195	98	51	69	50	—	12	463	22.6	6.6
	8	Starved	63†	49	32	0	0	1	—	5	81	15.4	2.3
12. iii. 51	15	Chlamydomonas	581	204	555	309	279	142	77	15	1566	30.5	17.4
	15	Dicrateria	547	16	1	102	37	26	18	11	200	16.8	2.5
	15	Chlorella	639	63	1			5	2	7	71	15.3	0.8
	15	Indian Ink	359	48	38	42	4	14	12	11	158	16.3	1.8
	8	Starved	208	50	3	2	28	0	22	6	105	19.8	2.2
22. iii. 51	15	Chlamydomonas	356	140	379	199	172	184	65	15	1139	26.6	12.8
	13	Hemiselmis	455	6	15	20	74	16	2	10	133	14.5	1.7
	15	Syracosphaera	277	271	356	88	70	186	45	15	1016	28.9	11.8
	15	Ditylum	328	329	347	109	181	366	90	15	1422	24.2	16.7
	8	Starved	251	28	0	0	0	3	3	2	34	28.0	0.8
23. iv. 51	13	Chlamydomonas	311	479	310	204	337	141	78	13	1549	32.1	20.7
	15	Lauderia	581	477	103	105	207	437	450	15	1779	33.4	21.2
	15	Gymnodinium	417	346	346	224	256	540	384	15	1974	29.9	21.9
	11	Starved	209	35	59	32	39	0	17	7	182	16.2	2.8

* Numbers below 5 omitted.

† Those of Chlamydomonas and 'starved' and three of those with Peridinium had been in the laboratory overnight and had probably laid their first batch of eggs.

Though the production of eggs depends on food, the relation between quantity of food and number of eggs produced is not a linear one, as Fig. 18 shows. In one experiment with a concentration of *Chlamydomonas* as low as 7-8 cells/mm³, egg production was much the same in fed as in starved *Calanus*. It increased rapidly with *Chlamydomonas* concentration up to about 40-80 cells/mm³ after which there was little further effect. Beyond a certain point more food will not produce more eggs.

The effect of different kinds of food on egg laying has been investigated by selecting ripe females, feeding them on various types of organisms and counting the number of eggs laid (Table I). Raymont and Gross (1942) first did this and tested both diatoms and small flagellates. It has been found at Millport that not all organisms are equally effective in egg production. All the diatoms tested (*Coscinodiscus centralis, Lauderia borealis, Skeletonema costatum, Rhizosolenia delicatula, Ditylum brightwelli, Chaetoceros pseudocrinitus, Nitzschia closterium*, var. *minutissima**) were good foods but of the other organisms (*Syracosphaera carterae, Peridinium trochoideum, Gymnodinium* sp., *Chlamydomonas* sp., a Chrysomonad flagellate B II (Raymon and Gross, 1942), *Hemiselmis rufescens, Dicrateria inornata* and *Chlorella stigmatophora*) the first five were good foods, the last three little better than starvation. Variations in the effectiveness of the foods provided may, in the laboratory, be caused by factors not operating in the sea e.g. *Coscinodiscus*, and to a less extent *Skeletonema*, sink to the bottom of the vessel and are therefore less available to the copepods. *Chlorella* however was taken into the gut in quantities but seemed to pass through most unaltered. It thus behaved like an inert substance such as Indian ink which also was passed through the gut in quantities but had no effect on egg production.

Neither a high pH value nor the addition of cell-free filtrate from a *Chlamydomonas* culture had any effect on egg laying. The results indicate therefore that metabolism is rapid and that the food taken is used immediately in the formation of eggs. This was confirmed by feeding ripe female *Calanus* on *Chlamydomonas* cells containing radio-active phosphorus. After only eight hours of such feeding the *Calanus* laid strongly radioactive eggs. An analysis of the animal showed that of the radio-active P retained about 50% was concentrated in the ovary and oviducts.

TIME OF EGG LAYING

The fact that eggs, nauplii and young stages are found mainly in the top 30 m led Nicholls (1933b) to suppose that the eggs were laid during the night when the *Calanus* migrated upwards, and this has since proved to be true (Harding, Marshall and Orr, 1951). The results of a series of

* This variety has now been identified as *Phaeodactylum tricornutum*.

observations on the time of the egg laying are shown in Fig. 19. About 100
ripe females were put singly into dishes holding 25 ml of sea water and the
number of females laying and of eggs laid were examined at hourly
intervals.

On 19th March 1951 (Fig. 19A) a haul was taken in the afternoon. At

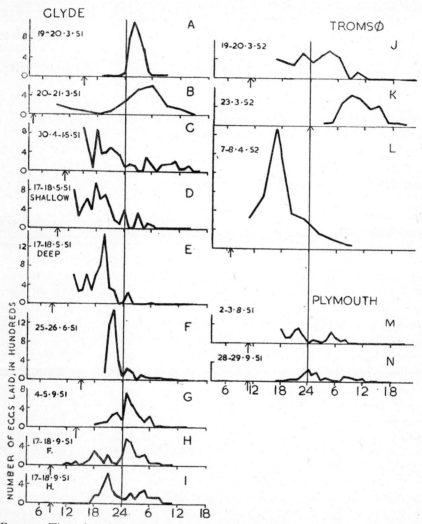

FIG. 19.   Time of egg laying in *Calanus* at different places and in different seasons. The
arrow shows the hour of capture.

that date the overwintering generation was just beginning to lay in the
sea. In the laboratory no eggs were laid before 10 p.m. and only 3 females

laid before midnight; 68% laid between midnight and 3 a.m. and most of the rest before 4 a.m. These *Calanus* had been caught about 4 p.m. but a haul of *Calanus* taken at 4 a.m. on the 20th also had their egg laying maximum between 12 and 4 a.m. the following night (Fig. 19B). This indicates that it was not caused by some stimulus having an effect a definite number of hours after capture, e.g. change of pressure.

The first generation of *Calanus* for the year, the offspring of the over-wintering population, reach maturity in the sea during April and May and are usually found near the surface during both day and night (see p. 124). Their spawning behaviour differs markedly from that of the previous generation for they lay throughout the 24 hours. Fig. 19C shows that egg production is decidedly irregular and that more spawning goes on between noon and midnight than at any other time of the day.

Even when most of the *Calanus* are at the surface, some are always found in deep water and the egg laying behaviour of these is shown in Fig. 19E together with that of some taken at the surface at the same time, Fig. 19D. Both lots have an extended period of spawning, again mainly between noon and midnight but there is a more marked maximum in the deep water *Calanus* between 7 and 8 p.m.

The second generation of *Calanus* in the Clyde, which grow up from the eggs spawned in May, retreat again to deep water and their egg laying behaviour (Fig. 19F) reverts to that found in March except that the peak of spawning comes between 9 and 10 p.m.

By September the over-wintering stock is being built up and most *Calanus* do not develop beyond Stage V. There are still ripe females present however and observations were made on their spawning behaviour; the results however were anomalous. Those of 4th September (Fig. 19G) which contained 5% *helgolandicus*, had a rather spread-out spawning period with a peak at 12-1 a.m. Those of 17th September contained 30% *helgolandicus* and the two forms behaved differently. In *finmarchicus* (Fig. 19H) spawning extended over most of the 24 hours though there was little before 5 p.m. or after 5 a.m. There were small peaks at 5-6 p.m. and 8-9 p.m., and a marked one at 12-1 a.m. In *helgolandicus* (Fig. 19I) spawning went on from 5 p.m. till 8 a.m. with a main peak at 8-9 p.m. and a smaller at 4-5 a.m.

Catches consisting entirely of *helgolandicus* were observed for egg laying at Plymouth in August and October. In August (Fig. 19M) they were caught at a depth of about 7 m and the number of eggs laid was rather low. They laid mainly between 5 and 11 p.m. and between 4 and 9 a.m. The October catch was got at a depth of about 10 m and eggs were laid in small quantities from 6 p.m. onwards, with the maximum between 10 p.m. and 2 a.m. (Fig. 19N).

Similar experiments were made with *Calanus* caught at Tromsø in the spring of 1952. The peak of egg laying did not come at any particular time of day or night but seemed to be dependent rather on the time of capture. Catches were made at 7 a.m., 10 a.m. and midnight (Fig. 19 J, K, L) and in all cases egg laying started almost at once and the peak came 9 to 12 hours later. It is possible that the stimulus to egg laying caused by capture and examination predominates in Tromsø waters whereas in the Clyde area the impulse to lay only during a particular part of the day is at times stronger.

It is surprising that quite a number of the *Calanus* laid twice in the 24 hours. A production of from 1 to 3 or 4 eggs was not unusual following closely on the laying of a considerable number and they were considered to be all one batch. Quite a number of females however laid considerable numbers twice or even three times within the 24 hours. This was especially marked in May when there was an abundant food supply in the sea water and 31% laid twice or three times with totals for the 24 hours up to 147. In March on the other hand when diatoms were scarce only 2% laid more than once. The other experiments were intermediate both in number of second lays and in food available in the sea.

Wimpenny (1938) supposed that reproduction in copepods took place more by day than during the night. His observations for *Calanus* were however averaged from cruises in June and October and it is therefore difficult to assess the results.

If the restricted period of egg laying is an adaptation to ensure that eggs are laid near the surface, one would expect it to be closely linked with diurnal vertical migration. This seems to be roughly true but we know far too little about the variations in this migration to make a strict comparison possible (see Chapter IX). There are differences in the migrations between the different developmental stages and there may also be differences between animals in different states of maturity. There is a kind of cycle apparent from the foregoing result in the Clyde sea area, i.e. the moving of the spawning period from about 1 a.m. in the overwintering population back to the afternoon in the first generation for the year and thereafter gradually forward to midnight again, but if studied at closer intervals quite a different pattern might be found. The results from September and October are confusing and this is not entirely because of a difference between *finmarchicus* and *helgolandicus*. A much closer study of the relation between diurnal vertical migration in females and egg laying is necessary before this can be cleared up.

D

CHAPTER IV

DEVELOPMENT

THE egg of *Calanus* is denser than sea water and will begin to sink as soon as it has been laid. Gross and Raymont (1942) have calculated that at a temperature of about 13°C it will sink at the rate of about 2·5 cm/min. A *Calanus* egg takes about 24 hours to develop and this means that if it is laid at the surface the nauplius will hatch at a depth of about 36 m. Eggs, nauplii and young copepodites are found mainly in the top 30 m (Nicholls, 1933b) and it seems probable that the restriction of egg laying in early spring to a short time at night (pp. 39-40), when the females are near the surface, may be an adaptation to allow the eggs to hatch as near the surface as possible.

In higher latitudes the colder water is more viscous and the eggs will sink more slowly. It is noteworthy that the eggs of the closely related *C. hyperboreus* do not sink in sea water and even in the laboratory remain suspended in the containing vessel.

Some experiments were made at Millport on the rate of sinking of the eggs of *C. finmarchicus* at different temperatures. The stage of development of the egg and small variations in size had no effect but the rate of sinking at 15°C was much greater than at 5°C, and at 5°C greater than at 0°C. There was a slight but distinct difference between the rates of fall of eggs from *C. finmarchicus* and *C. helgolandicus*, the first, which are slightly smaller, being slower. There were, however, great individual variations between eggs even of the same batch and these were occasionally great enough to mask the effects of temperature. The rates varied from between 1·25 and 2·5 cm/min at 0°C to between 1·6 and 6·8 cm/min at 20°C. The rate is probably much affected by the presence or absence of diatoms in the water. In culture these produce a mucus-like substance which slows down the rate of sinking very considerably.

INTERNAL DEVELOPMENT

The egg

Dr Harding has studied the egg from laying up to the first cleavage; the later development and the changes occurring internally up to the first or second copepodite stage were first described by Grobben (1881). The following account is taken chiefly from his paper. Judging from the size

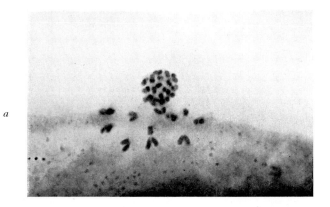

a

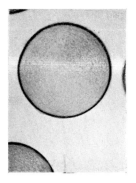

b

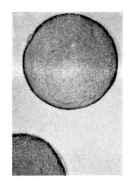

c

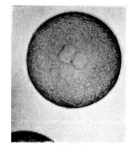

d

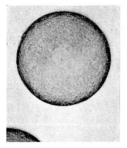

e

FIG. 20. Development of *Calanus* eggs (145 μ) up to first
cleavage (at 18°C).

(a) separation of first polar body from an egg about 5
minutes old, (b) egg 8 minutes old, (c) separation of second
polar body in egg 15 minutes old, (d) egg 22 minutes old
showing male and female pronuclei, (e) egg 29 minutes old
when nuclear membranes have disappeared.

of the eggs, Grobben was dealing with *C. helgolandicus* but there is not likely to be any appreciable difference in development between the two forms.

According to him the egg when newly laid has no membranes but when it becomes spherical, one appears. Its surface is covered with branching wrinkles and this, in optical section, gives the egg a spiny appearance. A second structureless membrane forms below this and the first membrane gradually smooths out. Even at hatching, however, we have seen the surface of the outer membrane to be wrinkled. Grobben says that before or during the formation of the first of these membranes the two polar bodies are extruded, usually one before and one after, so that one escapes and one is trapped below the outer membrane. Occasionally both polar bodies are so trapped. The polar body remains on the surface until about the 16-cell stage and then passes into the segmentation cavity and eventually disappears. This does not agree with Hilton's (1931) description of the polar bodies (see p. 31).

Dr Harding has found that by separating a clutch of freshly laid eggs into samples, one to be photographed at frequent intervals and the others to be fixed in turn, it is possible to correlate visible changes in the living egg with the cytological events. The sequence of changes in a clutch of eggs is beautifully synchronized provided all the eggs are kept at the same temperature; they seem to take place about two and a half times as rapidly at 18°C as they do at 8°C. As already mentioned (p. 31), in the newly laid eggs the anaphase chromosomes of the first maturation division are arranged on the metaphase plate. Fig. 20a shows the separation of the first polar body from an egg five minutes old at about 18°C. The second polar body appears about 9 minutes after laying and is shown in Fig. 20c where it can be clearly seen lying under the membrane. The male and female pronuclei appear quite suddenly near the centre of the egg (Fig. 20d) when it is about 18 minutes old and remain visible for about 10 minutes. Grobben describes both as moving, surrounded by rays, from the periphery to the centre of the egg and uniting there.

No chromosomes can be seen, according to Dr Harding, in most preparations made from eggs with visible pronuclei but at about the time the nuclear membranes disappear (Fig. 20e), when the egg is about 28-30 minutes old, prophase chromosomes appear in the form of long flexible filaments, 34 in number, often much spread out. By the time the egg is about 40 minutes old (at about 18°C), the first cleavage furrow (Fig. 21a) and the two nuclei of the daughter cells are visible.

Grobben takes the polar body as marking the animal pole and says that the first division is meridional and the second equatorial. Divisions continue at right angles to one another (Fig. 21b), giving rise to cells all of the

same size until the 32-cell stage when the future endoderm is delineated
by the oblique cleavage of one cell into a large and a small daughter cell.
The large one (*cen*), distinguished from the rest by its coarsely granular
protoplasm and large number of yolk globules, is the central endodermal
cell but the small one (*ven*) and the four cells surrounding these two will
also form part of the endoderm. The cell lying behind the central one (*u*)
contains the future mesoderm.

The egg has now a dorsal and a ventral surface, an anterior and posterior
end. The ventral side is marked by the central, and the anterior end by
the small, endoderm cell.

After about 2 hours (at 15-20°C) a segmentation cavity is well marked
(Fig. 21*c* and 22*b*) and it is bordered by all the cells except the small
anterior endoderm cell. The polar body (*r*) is still visible inside (Fig. 22*b*).
There is now a pause of several hours when no change is seen.

At this stage Grobben's figures show the central mass of large cells surrounded by a narrow rim formed by the edges of the underlying cells
(Fig. 22*a* and *c*). This appearance is readily seen in the living egg.

The central endoderm cell now divides and the mesoderm-containing
cells (*urms*) lying behind it also divide into a larger anterior and a smaller
posterior portion (Fig. 22*d*). The first are the original mesoderm cells and
the second are ectodermal. All three germ layers are now present. The large
and small endoderm cells with some of those (*sen*) immediately round them
(products of division of the original side-cells) will form all the endoderm,
the two mesoderm cells mentioned above give rise to all the mesoderm
and the remainder will form ectoderm. All three layers are bilaterally
symmetrical.

Gastrulation now takes place (Fig. 21*d* and 22*e*, *f*, *g*). The four mesoderm cells (*ms*) are first separated off to lie free in the segmentation cavity
(Fig. 22*e*). The endoderm cells (*en*) are then gradually pushed into it too,
along with a few of the nearest ectoderm cells (Fig. 22*f*). The ectoderm (*ec*)
grows gradually over the inwardly-pushing mass thus forming the gastrula
mouth (*gm*). Eventually the endoderm forms a small sac inside with the
mesoderm cells, still only four in number, between it and the ectoderm (Fig.
22*g*). The gastrula mouth lies longitudinally and is closed from the front
backwards. At 15-20°C the gastrula mouth is visible after about 8-10 hours.

At a later stage, although no external structure is visible (Fig. 21*e*), the
ventral side is a little flattened with the endodermal sac underlying it
(Fig. 22*h*). The mesoderm cells have divided to form a mass which will give
rise to the muscles which move the nauplius limbs. The ectoderm of the
anterior dorsal side (*dors*) has thickened to form the rudiment of the nervous
system. After the limb rudiments are distinct (Fig. 21*g*) the oesophagus
is formed by an invagination of the ectoderm joining the endodermal sac

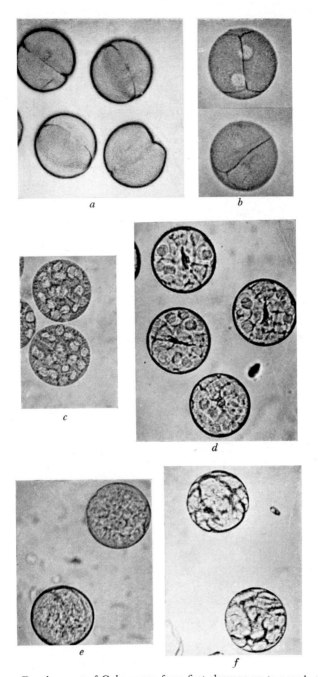

FIG. 21. Development of *Calanus* egg from first cleavage up to near hatching.
(a) two-cell stage, (b) four-cell stage showing nuclei, (c) segmentation cavity stage,
(d) gastrulation, (e) no macroscopic structure visible, (f) late nauplius form.

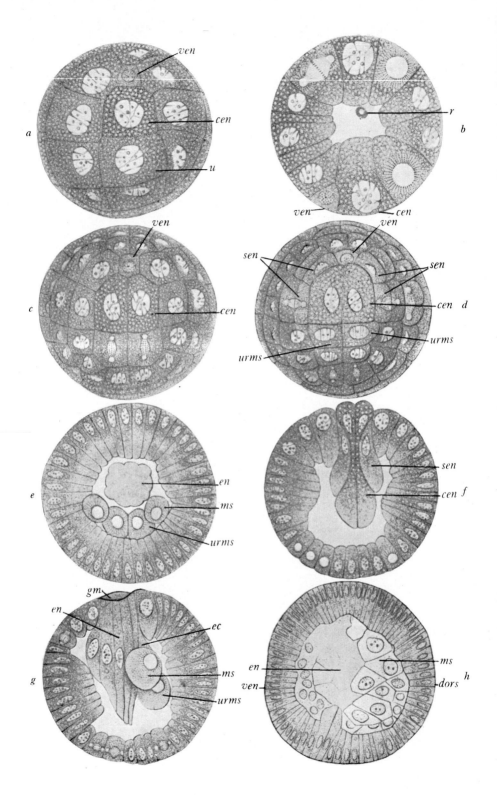

Fɪɢ. 22.   Stages in the development of the egg (Grobben).

(a) egg about the 32-cell stage from the ventral side, (b) egg about the same stage in optical section; the polar body is visible in the segmentation cavity, (c) a slightly later stage seen from the ventral side, (d) a later stage showing the first separation of the germ layers, (e) gastrula stage seen in transverse optical section, (f) gastrula stage seen in longitudinal optical section showing the central mesoderm cells in the middle, (g) gastrula from the side; the ectoderm is seen in optical section, (h) a later stage showing the limb rudiments, ectoderm and endoderm in optical section.

cen, central endoderm cell; dors, dorsal side; ec, ectoderm; en, endoderm; gm, gastrula mouth; ms, mesoderm cells; r, polar body; sen, side endoderm cells; u, urms, original mesoderm cells; ven, small endoderm cell.

and the labrum is formed at the same time. Later a space appears between embryo and shell and hatching then takes place (Fig. 23a-h).

When the nauplius is about to hatch, a faint twitching of the limbs is seen, then the outer membrane cracks and the inner membrane bulges out and gradually increases in volume (Fig. 23a-c). Finally the outer membrane slips off leaving the nauplius enclosed in the delicate inner membrane which has now expanded until there is a clear space between it and the nauplius (Fig. 23d and e). Whereas the egg diameter before hatching is about 145 μ the diameter of the inner membrane increases to about 245 μ, and the volume is thereby increased to about five times the original. While the membrane is expanding the nauplius gradually releases itself from its cramped position, the limbs stretch out and begin to move vigorously (Fig. 23f), and after a few moments the delicate membrane ruptures and crumples up and the nauplius is free (Fig. 23h). In the laboratory the whole process takes about 5 to 10 minutes. Sometimes more time is spent in hatching from the first membrane, sometimes from the second. It seems very probable that the mechanism of hatching is osmotic, the imbibition of water through the inner membrane causing an increase in pressure which ruptures the outer case. Excretion, or the release of some substance by the nauplius, might account for the imbibition. According to Yonge (1938) in the eggs of decapod crustacea the outer membrane is semi-permeable and the inner freely permeable.

Hatching, or at least the rupture of the outer membrane and the bulging out of the inner, can be induced by very slight dilution of the sea water. This happens only when the eggs are almost ready to hatch. The eggs of numerous other copepods hatch in much the same way (Marshall and Orr, 1954). Hall (1953) has described the method of hatching in *Chirocephalus* which is rather similar to that in *Calanus*.

The length of time from laying to hatching will depend largely on the temperature of the water and observations have been made at Millport, Plymouth and Tromsø on the rate of development at different temperatures. It was thought that *Calanus* living in the Arctic might be so adapted to low temperatures that their eggs would develop more quickly, but this proved not to be the case and on the whole development went on at much the same rate at similar temperatures in all the places where it was investigated.

Table II gives a rough approximation for the time taken to reach different stages in development. The stages listed in the Table are some of those most easily recognizable. The time taken for the egg to reach the two-cell, eight-cell, or hatching stage can be determined with some precision but the other stages may extend over a considerable time and their limits can be only approximately given. The characteristic appearance of some of the stages is shown in Fig. 21. Although the eggs in any one batch usually developed at much the same rate and those which hatched did so at much the same time, there were always some which did not reach hatching, and there was some variation in time between different batches of eggs. On one occasion the difference was considerable.

TABLE II

TIME OF DEVELOPMENT IN HOURS

	$0°$	$5°$	$10°$	$15°$	$20°$
2 cells - - - -	$2\frac{1}{2}$	—	$1\frac{1}{3}$	I	$\frac{3}{4}$
Segmentation cavity -	10-25	10-18	—	2-3	2-3
Gastrula mouth visible	25-50	16, 20-27	12	8-11	—
No structure visible -	50-70	25-40	—	14-20	12
Clear nauplius form -	90	27, 48	—	16-20	14-18
Hatching - - -	116-120	40*, 59-65	25-30	20-26	19-22

* One set of eggs hatched after 40 hours, eleven sets took 59-65 hours.

It will be noted that, if the eggs sink at the rates observed experimentally, those developing at low temperatures will be much below 50 m when they come to hatch. Since *Calanus* eggs at Tromsø in the Arctic are of much the same size as those in temperate waters and sink and develop at much the same rate, it remains a problem why the majority of *Calanus* eggs in the Arctic are still found mainly in the top 50 m.

The nauplius (Fig. 24)

In the newly hatched nauplius according to Grobben the mouth opens under the large labrum and a short oesophagus joins it to the gut which runs straight back to an ectodermal papilla on the dorsal side near the hind end. This papilla will later form the proctodaeum. Grobben believes that at this stage the gut is not open posteriorly. The nervous system is represented by pre- and post-oesophageal ganglia which are joined by a commissure and are still in contact with the body wall. The nauplius eye is a reddish-brown fleck on the surface of the anterior ganglion. In the ventrally curved, posterior end of the body are two mesoderm cells which are probably the beginnings of the genital system.

The internal changes in Nauplius II have not been described and Grobben's next stage is Nauplius III. Apart from the increasing length of the body and the larger number of spines and setae, there is a great development of the muscles which work the limbs. They all run from the limbs to a point on the dorsal surface which is marked by a branching reddish pigment cell. There is also a thickening of the ectoderm lying behind the eye and in contact with the pre-oesophageal ganglion (brain). The gut is much the same as in Nauplius I but is attached to the body

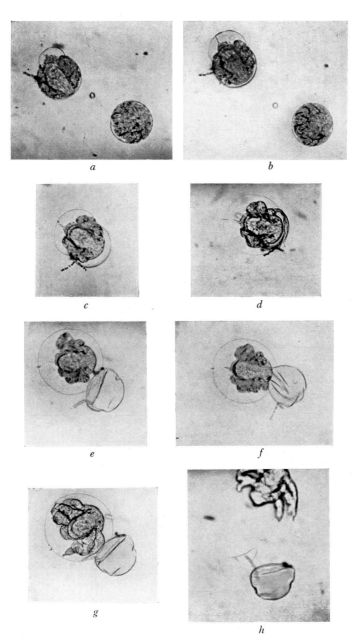

Fig. 23. The hatching of the egg. The orientation can be followed by the diatom chain sticking to the outer membrane.

(*a*) late nauplius-form egg (diameter 145 μ) and one with the inner membrane beginning to bulge, (*b*) the same at a slightly later stage, (*c*) the nauplius is moving forwards, (*d*) the outer membrane is crumpled up on the inner, (*e*) the inner membrane has slipped out completely and the outer has sprung back to its original shape, (*f*) the nauplius begins to expand, (*g*) the nauplius stretches its limbs, (*h*) the nauplius has burst out and is swimming away. The remains of the inner membrane are just visible above the outer.

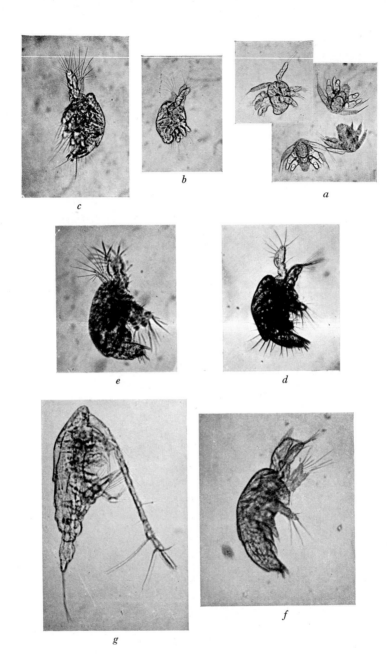

FIG. 24. Nauplius stages and Copepodite I, all to the same scale ($\times$ 50).
(a) Nauplius I, (b) Nauplius II, (c) Nauplius III, (d) Nauplius IV
(e) Nauplius V, (f) Nauplius VI, (g) Copepodite I.

wall dorsally and opens near the hind end of the now developed procto-daeum. The pair of mesoderm cells representing the beginnings of the genital system have moved anteriorly and lie on the ventral side of the gut. There are two small glands opening to the surface near the posterior end.

In the next stage described (probably Nauplius V) there are four of these glands. Each is formed of a single secretion-filled cell and they open separately on the ventral surface of the posterior end. The genital cells have moved still further forward into the last thoracic segment but they still lie ventral to the gut. They have now divided into a large cell with a large nucleus and nucleolus and several small cells of quite different form. The first will give rise to the germ cells, the second to the rest of the genital system. A carapace covers the front end of the body and includes the segment bearing the maxillipedes. The nervous system is now de-tached from the body wall and remains connected with it only by two bands of nervous tissue which stretch forward to the thickening behind the eye already described, which is now larger and stretches further dorsally. Grobben suggests that it may be the ganglion for a pair of com-pound eyes such as are found in related forms but which do not develop in copepods.

In the last nauplius stage (Nauplius VI) the most interesting internal change is in the position of the genital rudiment. The germ cells divide further and move gradually round the gut so that they lie first laterally, then dorsally and finally unite into a single flattened disc. The small surrounding cells do not all migrate with them but remain behind as a strand which will become the future genital duct. This stage is reached just before the final nauplius moult. An antennary gland is present, probably from the first nauplius onwards but it is very difficult to see until the later stages. It consists of a few basal cells and a hook-shaped duct hollowed out of a single cell. It opens on the coxa of the antenna.

The gut probably has a musculature from the beginning, but this is most clearly visible in Nauplius VI in which all the nuclei of the circular muscle fibres lie on the dorsal side. Strands of connective tissue run from the intersegmental areas to the gut. They are probably the rudiments of septa.

The copepodite (Fig. 25)

In the moult from nauplius to first copepodite several changes take place. The secondary ganglion loses its connection with the body wall and later becomes a mere projection on the brain. The ventral nerve cord is also detached from the body wall but it is impossible to say whether or not it is formed by the union of two separate strands. The anterior end of the brain is still connected to the frontal organs by strands of nervous tissue. The nauplius eye has withdrawn from the body wall.

The gonad is now an oval body lying dorsally to the gut in the first thoracic segment and owing to its growth the strands of tissue representing the ducts spring from the middle and not from the hind end as before. New organs appearing at this stage are the heart, formed between the first and second thoracic segments from paired mesodermal rudiments, and the maxillary glands. These have an angular end-sac and a curving duct like the adult (p. 21) and open at the base of the maxilla. The antennary glands now degenerate and disappear.

There are several interesting points in this development from egg to first copepodite. There is first the pause which takes place about the 16-cell stage. A pause seems also to occur in Nauplius III judging from the abundance of this stage in tow-nettings (see also Lebour, 1916). Secondly the early appearance of the genital cells is striking and also their paired condition and their gradual migration from the ventral to the dorsal side. Thirdly there is the development and disappearance of a secondary brain which may have been evolved to deal with compound eyes although these have now disappeared.

The changes occurring in internal development from first to fifth copepodite have not been described but are likely to be small.

External Development

Although many observations had been made on *Calanus* and although it was recognized as early as 1820 that the nauplius and early copepodite were stages in the development of copepods yet it was not until this century that a full description was published of all the stages through which *C. finmarchicus* passes. These are shown in Figs. 24 and 25.

Grobben did not carry his observations beyond Copepodite I and paid little attention to the external features. In 1848, however, Krøyer published a short description of some of the developmental stages in *C. hyperboreus* (which are closely similar to those of *C. finmarchicus*). He mistook Copepodite V for the adult and described Copepodites I-IV and two nauplii, one probably Nauplius VI and the other an earlier stage. He gave the number of segments in thorax and abdomen, the relative lengths of those parts, the number of swimming feet and, in some, the number of segments in the antennule.

It was left to a botanist, H. H. Gran (1902) to realize the importance of a knowledge of these younger stages in any study of the life history, as well as in the part which *C. finmarchicus* plays in the productivity of northern waters. A long series of measurements enabled him to separate the successive copepodite stages and he noted also the number of segments in the abdomen, but seems to have taken no account of the number of swimming feet. The separation and counting of these stages in the tow-nettings made it possible to recognize the areas and times of breeding in the Norwegian Sea.

He gave no drawings however, and it was not till 1916 that Lebour, from Crawshay's material, published drawings and descriptions of all the stages (except Nauplius VI) from egg to adult. In 1934 Sømme, working mainly on *C. hyperboreus*, amplified and in some cases corrected her observations.

Table III shows the number of free thoracic segments, of urosome segments and of swimming feet in the copepodite stages. These are the features by which the different stages are most easily distinguished. In copepodite Stages I and II there are two narrow segments which apparently belong to the urosome and they have been included in it by Gran (1902) and Damas (1905). Oberg however (1906) says that the first narrow segment divides at the first two copepodite moults, the anterior portion bearing the new pair of swimming feet, so that this segment must belong to the thorax. The urosome segment present from the first copepodite stages is morphologically the last, since the anus opens on it, and the morphological first does not appear until Copepodite III. In measurements of the metasome however, this last thoracic segment in Copepodites I and II has usually been excluded.

TABLE III

Copepodite stage - -	I	II	III	IV	V	VI
No. of free thoracic segments	4	5	5	5	5	5
No. of urosome segments -	1	1	2	3	4	♀4, ♂5
No. of pairs of swimming feet	2	3	4	5	5	5

Detailed descriptions and drawings of the adult animal are found in Giesbrecht (1892) and Sars (1903), and of the developmental stages in Lebour and Sømme. Drawings of appendages from one or more stages are found also in Claus (1863), Grobben (1881), With (1915), and other authors but they are not in general so accurate. On examining all these in detail it was found that the various authors rarely agreed completely. An examination was therefore made of a few specimens of each developmental stage of the *Calanus* from the Clyde sea area (Fig. 26 and Tables IV and V).

Sømme says that he examined at least ten specimens of each stage of *C. hyperboreus* and not quite so many of *C. finmarchicus* and that he found no variation at all either between the two species or between different specimens of the same stage. This is not true of the Clyde *Calanus* nor, to judge from the drawings of such careful observers as the above mentioned authors, is it true in general.

Some parts of some of the limbs remain unchanged throughout the greater part of their development. In the exopod of the mandible for instance there are 6 setae from Nauplius II up to the adult. In most parts of most of the mouth appendages, however, there is a gradual increase in the number of setae as development proceeds and it seems probable that even when the end result is the same, the steps by which it is reached may not always be so.

The main features of all the appendages and their developmental stages are tabulated on pp. 56-63; the most usual number of setae is given and the variability (including results from the authors mentioned above) indicated in brackets. On the whole the highest figures are probably the most accurate since it is very easy to miss setae either because they have been knocked off or because they are lying on top of one another. Gurney's (1931) views on the segmentation are adopted in Tables IV and V. The appendages are shown in Fig. 26 and some notes on their structure are given below.

Antennule (Fig. 26)

The three setae on the three prominences of segment 2 may be present in Nauplius I, but since there are in this stage no lateral setae on the end segment to keep the limb flat, it does not always lie so that they can be seen.

Antenna (Fig. 26)

From Nauplius III-VI the coxa bears two very strong spiny setae (masticatory processes) and the basipod one. That on the basipod bends back so that all three lie close together resembling the teeth on the maxillular gnathobase as it is seen in later stages. They disappear completely in the copepodite stages when the mandibular and maxillular gnathobases are fully developed and have presumably taken over their function.

Lebour describes the exopod as 7-segmented from Nauplius II onwards, and it is certainly 7-segmented in the adult. In Nauplius V and VI however, Sømme describes it as 8-segmented and it is so in the Clyde specimens too. Since in the nauplius the terminal segment is very short and has 3 setae, whereas in copepodite stages it is longer than those preceding it and has a lateral seta as well as 3 terminal, it seems probable that, in moulting from nauplius to copepodite, the two distal segments have fused.

There is also a curious point in the position of the setae on the two proximal segments of the exopod. From Copepodite I to IV there is one on the most proximal and three on the next but in Copepodites V and VI there are two on each segment.

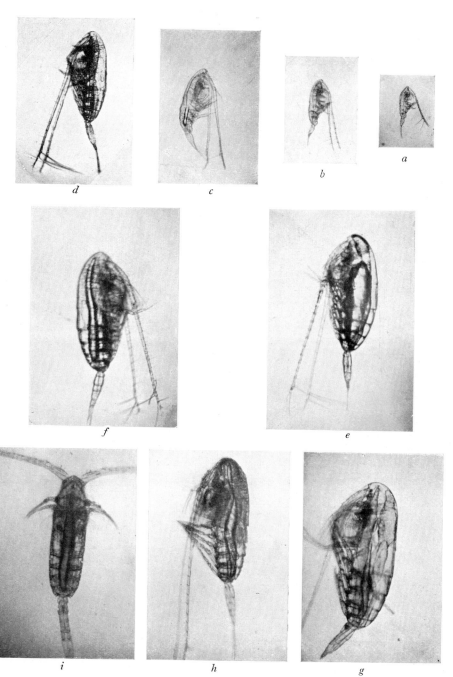

FIG. 25.   Copepodite stages all to the same scale ($\times 15$).
(*a-d*) Stages I to IV, (*e*) fat and (*f*) thin Stage V, (*f*) is the *helgolandicus* form as shown by
the pointed head, (*g*) female, (*h*) and (*i*) lateral and dorsal view of male.

Mandible (Fig. 26)

Beginning as a prominent bulge in the early nauplius stages, in the later the gnathobase becomes a long curving process bearing a seta and ending

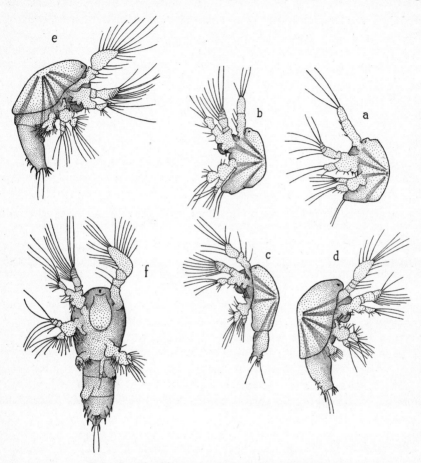

FIG. 26.   Nauplius stages to show the appendages.

(*a*) Nauplius I, limbs from the front end backwards, antennule, antenna, mandible, (*b*) Nauplius II, limbs as in (*a*), (*c*) Nauplius III, limbs as in (*a*), (*d*) Nauplius IV, limbs as in (*a*) with the rudiment of the maxillule, (*e*) Nauplius V, limbs as in (*d*), rudiment of *p.* 1 just visible, (*f*) Nauplius VI from the ventral side, each limb shown on one side only, left hand side: antennule, maxillule, maxillipede and *p.* 1, right hand side; antenna, mandible, maxilla and *p.* 2.

in 2 or 3 teeth. The copepodite gnathobase is relatively much shorter and can be seen developing under the skin of the last nauplius stage with its toothed edge almost parallel to the long axis of the process.

The number of setae on the basipod seems to be variable.

Maxillule (Fig. 26)

This complicated appendage appears in Nauplius IV as a two-lobed flap with setae, but in Nauplius V has almost its final form. There is usually however only one internal lobe present. Sømme queries the presence of a second, and in one of the Clyde specimens there seemed to be a second with 1 seta, lying under the first with 2. In Nauplius VI although Lebour and Sømme both mention only 2 setae on each lobe most of the Clyde specimens have 4 as in the adult. The number of setae on the epipod, endopod and exopod increase with increasing growth as do also the teeth on the gnathobase although these are more variable in number.

Maxilla (Fig. 26)

Appearing in Nauplius V as a pair of lobes, the appendage takes on almost the adult form in Nauplius VI. It consists of three main segments bearing a series of six lobes, each lobe with a group of setae, and an end part divisible into three segments. Following Gurney (1931) the first two lobes are considered as belonging to the coxa, the next two to the basipod and the fifth and sixth to the endopod. The sixth lobe is small and, although attached to the preceding one, lies above the third endopod segment and has sometimes been taken to belong to it.

In each group of setae one seta is spinier than the rest and lies at an angle across them. On endopod segments 3 and 4 these cross-setae are not easy to see in the early stages and may sometimes perhaps be absent. Gurney says that there is little, apart from the view that the protopod is three-segmented, to make one put the fifth and sixth lobes in the endopod and they are taken by Giesbrecht and Borradaile to belong to the basipod.

On the most proximal lobe of all and on the two endopod lobes the number of setae increases during development but on the rest it may be complete from the beginning.

Maxillipede (Fig. 26)

There has been some difference of opinion about the origin of the segments of this limb. In dissection the first segment is often lost. Giesbrecht takes the segment with 3 setigerous lobes to be the first, and the next segment, together with the papilla bearing 2 setae, to be the second, basipod. Borradaile takes the actual first and the three-lobed segment to represent a four-segmented protopod and all the rest an abnormally segmented endopod. Gurney takes the small papilla with 2 setae to belong to the endopod for it is found, sometimes in *Calanus* and often in other copepods, as a separate segment. Sømme differs from all other observers in the large number of terminal setae in Copepodite I (7 as against

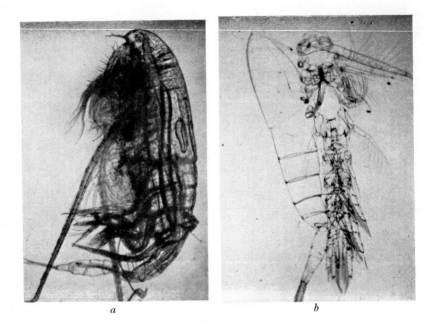

a   b

FIG. 27.

(a) Copepodite IV moulting to V; the back has been cast off and the antennules and urosome are partly withdrawn, (b) cast of Copepodite V.

the usual 4) and he too describes the 'endopod' with six segments in Copepodite V.

Swimming feet (Fig. 4)

The different authors agree well in their descriptions of these limbs and the slight differences which do occur are mainly differences of nomenclature.

The long curly seta which occurs on the basipod of *p.* 1 appears first in Copepodite II.

In some segments there is variability in the number of setae present. A well recognized instance of this is in the adult *p.* 5 where the number of external setae on the last segment of the endopod may be either 1 or 2 (see p. 14).

The difference between *C. finmarchicus* and *C. helgolandicus* in the form of the inner edge of the coxa in *p.* 5 of Stage V and female has been mentioned on p. 5.

A study of the mouth parts shows that the nauplius, at least in the early stages, must have quite a different feeding mechanism from the copepodite.

In Nauplius I, although the end setae are well developed on all the limbs, the lateral setae are mostly relatively short, extremely feeble and difficult to find. It is not until Nauplius III that the masticatory bristles on the basal joints of the antennae develop into anything that looks capable of catching or retaining food particles. Although Grobben does not mention the muscles in Nauplius I they are visible and well developed; the nauplius swims actively and can leap away from the mouth of a pipette with relatively as much agility as the adult. These active movements must set up water currents and it would be interesting to find out how these differ from the currents set up by the adult mouth parts, and their relation to feeding. It is possible that Nauplius I, and perhaps also Nauplius II, feed little or not at all. Nauplius I moults into Nauplius II after less than 24 hours and Grobben says that the gut has no anal opening in Nauplius I. This needs confirmation however, since some observers think they have seen the Nauplius I gut with greenish food material in it.

MOULTING

When a *Calanus* copepodite moults the exoskeleton splits horizontally just above the rostrum and the junction of the limbs, and the cephalosome is pushed back off the head like a hood (Fig. 27). Through this opening the *Calanus* slips out and the process usually occurs very rapidly. *Calanus* which takes a long time over it, or are found swimming with the moult attached, are almost certain to die. Dr D. T. Gauld has pointed out that one of the most frequent causes of failure is that the front part of the head sticks when the antennules have been partly withdrawn, the area between the roots of these limbs forming a band which holds them tightly together. In newly moulted *Calanus* one can quite often see that the antennules are extended not horizontally but lying close together longitudinally and they sometimes have a slight bend in them (Fig. 27*a*). In discarded moults the antennules are joined to one another as usual so that no fracture normally occurs here (Fig. 27*b*).

Currie (1918) has described what happens to the setae during moult. She says that the eating and swimming appendages are first drawn back a little from the old skin and that the setae, when they have loosened themselves, are drawn back into the body of the appendage 'as if they were being turned inside out from their bases'. When their tips have reached the level of the body however the pressure inside becomes so great that the old skin cracks and the setae are forced out once more, this time pushing the old skin away. The setae of the caudal rami extend themselves rather differently for the pressure in the tips of the rami themselves is so great that the bases of the setae are pushed out first, forming cylinders round their protruding tips. Gradually the whole seta is pushed out and straightened. Several of her figures show the old skin of a seta being thrown right off but normally the whole exoskeleton is cast in one piece and complete in every detail.

Specimens are occasionally found in which the tip of the antennule has obviously been damaged and has regenerated during moult. In all cases the result was not a normal antennule but one which ended in a little bunch of setae (see Rose, 1933). If regeneration should result in a normal limb it would of course be unnoticed.

Causes of moult

It is an interesting fact that, although the moulting of the over-wintering stock does not begin in the sea until the end of December or later, Stage V, when brought into the laboratory in autumn, almost always moult within one or two weeks. Several factors might be responsible for this, of which the most obvious are light, food, and warmth. The moulting of the winter stock seems to begin in December-January irrespective of latitude, and, since this coincides roughly with the turn of the year, one might expect light to be an important factor in the sea. Many of the *Calanus* however live in winter at such depths that the alteration in light must be extremely small but Sømme does think that this is the cause of the migration towards the surface which occurs in spring (see p. 123). A higher temperature and more food are factors which are not likely to operate in the sea in December.

A number of experiments were made, some with the collaboration of

Dr A. G. Nicholls, to test the effect which these factors had on the moult in the laboratory. They led to no very definite results.

Each factor tested seemed to have some positive effect, i.e. those in the light moulted better than those in the dark, those fed than those starved, and those at aquarium temperature better than those near o°C. It may be that the moult is caused by a number of different factors working together. On the whole however no conclusion can be drawn about the cause of the earlier moult in the laboratory when compared with the sea. Since a knowledge of this cause might lead to a better understanding of events in the sea in early spring the subject is well worth further study.

SEGMENTATION A

Numbers alone = seta..., s = spine; mp = masticatory process; + indicates separa

	N I	N II	N III	N IV	N V	N
Antennule						
No. of segments	3	3	3	3	3	3
No. of setae:						
1st segment	0	0	0	0	0	0
2nd segment Group 1	1 (0-1)	1	1	1	1	1
,, 2	1 (0-1)	1	1	1	1	1
,, 3	1 (0-1)	1	1	1	1	1
3rd ,, Ventral	3	0	1	3	4	
Dorsal	0	0	2	4	6	8
Terminal	3	4	4	4	4	4
Antenna						
Coxa	1 mp, 1 s (0-1)	1-2 mp, 1 s	2 mp, 1 s	2 mp, 1 s	2 mp, 1 s	2 mp
Basipod 1	Bulge 2 (0-2)	Bulge 1 mp, 1 s	Bulge 1 mp, 2 s	1 mp, 2 s	1 mp, 2 s	1 mp
2	Bulge 1 (0-1)	Bulge 1	Bulge 1	2	2 (1-2)	2 (1
Endopod 1	1 (0-1)	2 (1-2)	3 (1-3)	3 (2-3)	4 (3-4)	
2 lateral						2
terminal	2	3	4	4 (1 thin)	5 (2 thin)	3
Exopod 1	0	0	0	0	0	0
2	1	1	2	3	3 (2-3)	4 (3
3	1	1	1	1	1	1
4	1	1	1	1	1	1
5	1	1	1	1	1	1
6	2	1	1	1	1	1
7		2	3	3	1	1
8					3	
Total	6	7	9	10	11	12
Mandible						
Coxa	Bulge (0-1 s)	Bulge 1 s	Process 1 s	3 toothed process 1 s	2-3 toothed process 1 s	2-3 toothed process 1
Basipod	Bulge 2 (1-3)	Bulge 1 thick, 1 thin (1-2)	Bulge 1 thick, 2 or 3 thin	Bulge 1(1-2) thick, 4 (3-5) thin	Bulge 1-2 mp 4 or 5	1 5
Endopod 1	2 (1-2)	3	3 (1 thick mp)	4 1 mp	3+2	3
2	(1-2)+2	2+3	2+4	2+4	2+4	2
Exopod 1	1	2 (1-2)	2	2	2	2
2	1	1	1	1	1	
3	1	1	1	1	1	2
4	2	2	2	2	2	
5						
Total	5	6	6	6	6	6

ETATION OF APPENDAGES

roups of setae; variation shown in brackets; ext = external; term = terminal.

C I	C II	C III	C IV	C V	C VI
10	17 (12)	22 (16)	25 (23)	25	25*
17	26	33	54	55	55

For copepodite stages, only the total number of setae is shown

C I	C II	C III	C IV	C V	C VI
1	1	1	1	1	1
2	2 (2-3)	2	2	2	2
2	2	2	2	2	2
4 (4-6)	4 (4-6)	5 (6)	6 or 7	8	8 (7)
6 (4-6)	6 (5-7)	6 or 7	6 or 7 (5-7)	7	7 (7-8)
1	1	1	1	2	2
3	3	3	3	2	2
1	1	1	1	1	1
1 (1-2)	1	1	1	1	1
1	1	1	1	1	1
1	1	1	1	1	1
+ 3 term	1 + 3 term	1 + 3 term	1 + 3 term	1 + 3 term	1 + 3 term
12	12	12	12	12	12
nathobase	Gnathobase	Gnathobase	Gnathobase	Gnathobase	Gnathobase
small s	1 small s	1 small s	1 small s	1 small s	1 small s
4	4	4	4	4	4
4	4	4	4	4	4
6	6	8 (7-8)	9 (8-9)	10	10
1	1	1	1	1	1
1	1	1	1	1	1
1	1	1	1	1	1
1	1	1	1	1	1
2	2	2	2	2	2
6	6	6	6	6	6

24 in the ♂.

Numbers alone = setae; s = spine; mp = masticatory process; + indicates separat[e]

	N I	N II	N III	N IV	N V	N V[I]
Maxillule						
Precoxa, gnathobase					0-2 low teeth	4-8
Coxa 1st endite					2 or 3 (1-3)	3 or 4
1st exite					0	1
Basipod 1, 2nd endite					0-1	4 (2...
2nd exite						
2					2 or 3	2 or...
Endopod 1				5 (4-5)	2	2 (1...
2					2+4	2+...
Exopod				3	5	7
Maxilla						
Coxa, endite 1						3 (2...
,, 2						3 (2...
Basipod, ,, 3						3 (2...
,, 4						3 (2...
Endopod 1 ,, 5						2 (1...
2 ,, 6						0 or...
3						1
4						2
5						3
Maxillipede†						
Basipod 1 Group 1						0
,, 2						
,, 3						
2						0
Endopod 1						2
2						
3						
4						
5						
6						
Caudal armature						
Feelers	2	2	2	2	2	2
Ventral hooks			2	4	4	4
End hooks			2	2	2	2
Lateral hooks				6	6	6
Small spines			3 rows	3 rows	3 rows	3 ro[ws]

(N III column: *Beginning to show*)
(N V column, Maxilla: *Showing as lobes with spines*)

† Coxa bears no setae.

TATION OF APPENDAGES

ups of setae; variation shown in brackets; ext = external; term = terminal.

C I	C II	C III	C IV	C V	C VI
o (6-11)	7-11	9-12	11-14	12-14	12-15
4 (2-4)	4 (2-4)	4 (3-4)	4 (3-4)	4	4
4 (3-4)	6 (5-7)	8 (7-8)	9	9	9
4 (2-4)	4 (2-4)	4 (2-4)	4 (2-4)	4	4
I	I	I	I	I	I
3	3 (3-4)	4 (3-4)	4	4	4
2	2	3 (3-4)	3	4 (3-4)	4 (3-4)
+5 (4-5)	2+5 (3-5)	3+6 (6-7)	3+6 (5-6)	4+7 (6-7)	4 (3-4)+7
7	7	8 (7-8)	9 (7-9)	10	11 (11-12)
4 (3-4)	4	4 or 5	4 or 5	4-6	4-6
+1 ext	3+1 ext	3+1 ext	3+1 ext	3+1 ext	3+1 ext
3	3	3	3	3	3
3	3	3	3	3	3
4-5	4	4	4	4	4
I	I	1-3	1-2	1-2	1-3
I	I	1-2	2	2	2
2	2	2	2	2	2
3	3	3	3	3	3
I	3	3	3	3	3
2	3-4	4	4	4	4
2	3	4 (3-4)	4	4	4
2	3	3	3	3	3
2	2	2	2	2	2
I	I	I	2	3	4 large
4	I	I	2	3	4
	4	1+1 ext	I	2	3
		4	1+1 ext	2+1 ext	3+1 ext‡
			4	4	4¶

the ♂ the external seta is enlarged and reflexed.
the ♂ the two external setae are enlarged and the outermost reflexed.

TABLE V

SEGMENTATION AND SETATION OF SWIMMING FEET

s = seta; t = thorn; bl = blade; ext = external; int = internal; prox = proximal; term = terminal

		C I	C II	C III	C IV	C V	C VI
Pes I							
Coxa	Ext		1 s	1 s	1 s	1 s, no fringe	1 s
	Int						
Basipod	Ext		0-1 t	0-1 t	0-1 t	0-1 t	1 s
	Int		1 s	1 s	1 s	1 s	1 s
Endopod 1	Ext				Bulge	Bulge	Bulge
	Int				1 s	1 s	1 s
							1 small t
2	Ext	1 s	0-1 s	1 s	1 s	2 s	2 s
	Int		1 s	1 s	1 s	1 s	1 s
3	Ext	4 s	4 s	5 s	5 s	3 s	3 s
	Int	2 s	2 s	2 s	2 s	2 s	2 s
	Term						
Exopod 1	Ext	3-4 long t	1 long t	1 long t	1 long t	1 long t	1 long t
	Int	3 s	1 s	1 s	1 s	1 s	1 s
2	Ext		2-3 t	3 long t	3 long t	1 long t	1 long t
	Int			1 s	1 s	1 s	1 s
3	Ext					2 long t	2 long t
	Int		4 s	4 s	4 s	4 s	4 s
	Term	1 bl and sometimes 1 t	1 s	1 s	1 s	1 s	1 s
Pes II							
Coxa	Ext		1 s	1 s	1 s	1 s, fringe	1 s
	Int						
Basipod	Ext	1 t	1 t	1 t	1 t	1 t	1 t
	Int						

TABLE V—continued

	CI	CII	CIII	CIV	CV	CVI
Pes II—continued						
Endopod 1 Ext					1 t	1 t, fringe
1 Int					1 s	1 s
2 Ext		0-1 s	0-1 s	0-1 t	1 t	1 t, fringe
2 Int		2 s	2 s	1 s	2 s	2 s
3 Ext	1 s	2-3 s	4 s	2 s	4 s	2 s, fringe
3 Int	3-4 (1 prox)			5 s		4 s
Term	1 s	2 s	2 s	2 s	2 s	2 s
Exopod 1 Ext					2 t	2 t
1 Int					1 s	1 s, fringe
2 Ext	3 t	1-2 t	2 t	2 t	2 t	2 t
2 Int			1 s	1 s	1 s	1 s, fringe
3 Ext	3 s	2-3 t	3 or 5 t	3 or 5 t	2 t	2 t
3 Int	1 toothed bl	4 s	5 s	5 s	5 s	5 s, fringe
Term	1 t	1 bl, 1 t	1 bl, 1 t	1 bl, 1 t	1 bl, 1 t	1 bl, 1 t
Pes III						
Coxa Ext			1 s	1 s	1 s, fringe	1 s, fringe
Int						
Basipod Ext		1 t	1 t	1 or 2 t	1 t	1 t
Int						
Endopod 1 Ext					1 small t	1 small t, fringe
1 Int					1 s	1 s
2 Ext			0-1 t	0-1 t	1 t	1 large t, fringe
2 Int			1 s	1 s	2 s	2 s
3 Ext		1 s	2 s	2 s	2 s	2 s
3 Int		3 s	3 s	4 s	4 s	4 s
Term		2 s	2 s	2 s	2 s	2 s

61

TABLE V—continued

	C I	C II	C III	C IV	C V	C VI
Pes III—continued						
Exopod 1 Ext					2 t	2 t, fringe
Int					1 s	1 s, fringe
2 Ext			2 t	2 t	2 t	2 t, fringe
Int				1 s	1 s	1 s, fringe
3 Ext		3 t	2 t	3 t	2 t	2 t, fringe
Int		3 s	4 s	5 s	5 s	5 s, fringe
Term		1 bl, 1 t	1 bl, 1 t	1 bl, 1 t	1 bl, 1 t	1 bl, 1 t
Pes IV						
Coxa Ext				1 s	1 s, fringe	1 s
Int						
Basipod Ext			1 t	1 t, 1 hair	1 t, 1 hair	1 t, 1 hair
Int						
Endopod 1 Ext				1 t	1 t	1 t, fringe
Int			1 s	1 s	1 s	1 s
2 Ext					1 t	1 t, fringe
Int				2 s	2 s	2 s
3 Ext			1 s			3 s
Int			3 s	3 s	3 s	
Term			2 s (1 prox)	2 s	2 s, 1 t	2 s
Exopod 1 Ext					2 t	2 t, fringe
Int					1 s	1 s, fringe
2 Ext				2 t	2 t	2 t, fringe
Int					1 s	1 s, fringe
3 Ext			2-3 t	3 t	2 t	2 t, fringe
Int			3 s	5 s	5 s	5 s, fringe
Term			1 bl, 1 t	1 bl, 1 t	1 bl, 1 t	1 bl, 1 t

TABLE V—*continued*

Pes V

		C I	C II	C III	C IV	C V	C VI ♀	♂
Coxa	Ext				a few scattered teeth	numerous teeth	numerous teeth	As ♀
	Int							
Basipod	Ext				1 t, 1 hair	1 t, 1 hair	1 t, 1 hair	As ♀
	Int							
Endopod 1	Ext						1 t, fringe	1 small t
	Int						1 s, fringe	1 s
2	Ext					1 t	1 t, fringe	1 small t
	Int					1 s	1 or 2 s, fringe	1 s
3	Ext					2 s	1 or 2 s, fringe	2 s
	Int				3 s (1 prox)	3 s	2 s, fringe	2 s
	Term				2 s	2 s, 1 t	2 s, 1 t	2 s, 1 t
Exopod 1	Ext							
	Int						2 t	2 t
2	Ext					2 t	2 t, fringe	2 t
	Int						1 s, fringe	
3	Ext				2 t	2 t	2 t, fringe	2 t
	Int				3 t / 3 s	5 s	4 s, fringe	
	Term				1 bl, 1 t	1 bl, 1 t	1 bl, 1 t	1 short bl, 1

63

CHAPTER V

LIFE CYCLE

ALTHOUGH *Calanus* is very widely distributed over most of the oceans of the world its centre of abundance is in the north, and it is in the North Atlantic and Norwegian Sea that most work has been done on its annual life cycle. Round Greenland and Iceland, and off northern Norway it seems likely that pure *C. finmarchicus* is being dealt with; elsewhere it may be mixed with *helgolandicus*. However, a survey of the results from places where the reproductive cycle has been studied throughout the year indicates that both forms behave in much the same way (Rees, 1949).

The places where this type of investigation of the life cycle have been made are fortunately scattered over most of the region where *Calanus* is abundant, and range from the Barents Sea (Bogorov, 1933, 1938; Bogorov and Preobrajenskaya, 1934; Jaschnov, 1939; Manteufel, 1941); and the fjords of East Greenland (Ussing, 1938; Digby, 1954) to the St. Lawrence (Filteau, 1947, 1948, 1949) and the Gulf of Maine (Fish, 1936). Much work has been done on the Norwegian coast (Sømme, 1934, in the Lofoten area; Ruud, 1929, off Möre; Runnstrøm, 1932, in the Herdla and Hjelte Fjords near Bergen; and Wiborg, 1934, in the Oslo Fjord and 1954 off western Norway). Round Great Britain such observations have been made in the English Channel (Russell, 1928*b*; Bogorov, 1934), off the S.W. of Ireland (Farran, 1927) and the Clyde sea area (Nicholls, 1933*a*; Marshall, Nicholls and Orr 1934); Gibbons (1933) has studied the life cycle from hauls taken in the northern North Sea and Wimpenny (1937) in the southern North Sea whereas Rees (1949) has studied the whole of the North Sea from plankton recorder hauls.

Damas (1905) was among the first to study the life cycle and he supposed that *Calanus* in the Norwegian Sea was carried in a large circle from the polar regions south to the Faroe-Iceland channel and that breeding began where this current met Atlantic water. The new generation was carried north again up the Norwegian coast. The course of events has proved to be not quite so simple as this.

As is natural, the lower the temperature the slower is the rate of development, and the later does the first spawning occur but the latitude is not always a guide to the temperature of the water. Although the most northerly waters in East Greenland and the Barents Sea are also the coldest, those off the Norwegian fjords little farther south are much influenced by the Gulf Stream; again the southerly waters of the Gulf of Maine are, because of the cold Labrador current, lower in temperature than those of Plymouth and the Clyde.

The most convenient starting point for a description of the life cycle is in the dark winter months when development is almost at a standstill. Reproduction is over for the year and the stock which survives the winter will produce the first generation in the following spring. The composition of this stock varies from one latitude to another; in the more southerly areas (Gulf of Maine, Plymouth, the Clyde) it is almost entirely copepodite Stage V; as one goes farther north it is younger so that in the fjords of East Greenland the winter is passed in Stages III to V.

The winter population is normally found in deep water but observations on depth distribution have not often been made frequently enough to give an accurate picture of the seasonal movements. In East Greenland the winter hauls were taken through a hole in the ice by hauling a vertical net several times from 50 m to the surface and from 25 m to the surface; the *Calanus* lived mainly below 50 m although a considerable number were found above 50 and even above 25 m, throughout the winter. In the Lofoten area *Calanus* in winter is most abundant below 300 m, although it is present in considerable numbers between 300 and 200 m, and is scarce in waters above this, so much so that its winter distribution is practically confined to areas where there are depths of over 200 m. In the Herdla and Hjelte fjords it is found mainly below 100 m in winter (the fjords have a maximum depth of 400 m) and in the Oslo fjord the depth distribution is rather irregular but it is found deeper in winter than in summer. In the Clyde area too it retreats to deeper water in winter and is found mainly below 100 m.

Roussel de Vauzème (1834) who found immense concentrations of *Calanus* at the surface in February in the South Atlantic (Tristan da Cunha to Cape Horn), mentions that the sailors of the whaling ship told him that the *Calanus* lived in deep water in October and November, coming to the surface after that to lay their eggs.

In December or January moulting begins: it is interesting to note that this date does not seem to vary with latitude. Adults have been recorded in January and February in all regions from the English Channel north to East Greenland. Males appear first and usually predominate for a short time, then females appear and copulation takes place. This moulting and copulation take place early in the year in all the regions investigated although in East Greenland it is only a fraction of the winter stock, i.e. those copepods which had reached Stage V in the previous autumn, that can moult so early. There follows a period during which the female matures the eggs, then spawning takes place, the new generation grows up and the cycle is complete. The time taken for the whole cycle depends partly on the temperature and is short in the Channel and the Clyde sea area where it takes about two months, one month for development from egg to adult and up to one month for maturing the eggs. In the Gulf of Maine the cycle takes about $2\frac{1}{2}$ months, in Norwegian waters off Möre about three and in East Greenland it takes a whole year and possibly longer in some cases. In temperate waters (Plymouth, the Clyde sea area, the North Sea, the Gulf of Maine and southern parts of the Norwegian coast) spawning occurs in March or from March to April and there is time for two or even three more generations before the autumn.

It will be convenient to give a detailed account of the seasonal cycle at two of the places differing most widely, Loch Striven (Clyde sea area) and East Greenland, and to summarize the observations from the other regions.

In Loch Striven observations in 1933 were made weekly from January to September by means of vertical hauls with a quantitative net of the finest bolting silk (77 meshes/cm) from the bottom (about 70 m) to the surface (Figs. 28 and 29). Five hauls were taken each time; any that seemed very different from the rest were rejected and those remaining were mixed before counting. For part of the year (27th March-21st August) one haul was divided at 10 m. As was found later (Marshall 1949; Barnes 1949) the divided haul was usually poorer than the others owing to the method of closing the net, and was often rejected in taking the average although the vertical distribution was necessarily estimated from it.

On 17th January one quarter of the catch was adult with females predominant and in succeeding weeks this proportion increased until on 6th February 69% were adult, the rest being Stage V. Eggs were scarce until the middle of February and from then on the early copepodites of the new generation began to appear, but the majority of eggs were not laid till March and the brood grew up in March and early April. The first eggs were laid before the spring diatom increase when there was little microplankton in the water and although they did not grow up they appear to contradict later findings and laboratory experiments (pp. 34-36). Considering the large number of late copepodites and adults of this generation on 1st May, the numbers during the early part of its development seem much too low, but the early copepodites were then almost all above 10 m and the diatoms of the spring increase (which lasted from 13th March to 17th April) would clog the net in this part of the haul and so reduce the catch.

The early part of this generation reached Stage V in April and some of them moulted and spawned that month. The resulting brood apparently did not grow up and most of the first generation did not spawn till the

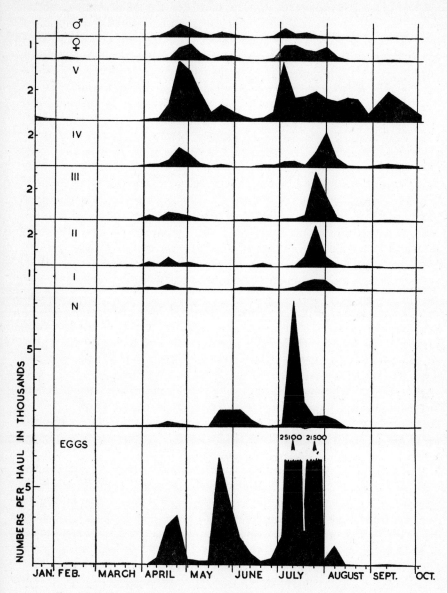

FIG. 28. Numbers of each stage of *Calanus* in Loch Striven˙in 1933.

end of May. This delay in moulting to adult, and abortive production of eggs is unusual and may have been caused by lack of food in the water (see p. 75). In normal years the first generation spawns in late April and early May. The second generation grew up during June and spawned in July. Most of the copepods resulting from this third generation did not complete their development but remained as Stage V and the few which did become adult produced only a small number of eggs which in turn developed only as far as Stage V and joined the others to make up the over-wintering stock.

In Fig. 28 are shown the actual numbers of each Stage throughout the year, and in Fig. 29 the percentages. When, as is the case in the Clyde area, the stock is homogeneous and there is no invasion from other areas, at least during the period shown (see p. 6), the percentage type of diagram evens out violent fluctuations in total numbers and enables one to follow the succession of stages when numbers are low. Thus for example the first generation of the year, from the eggs produced from February to March, does not show in Fig. 28 but is clear in Fig. 29; the same is true when the second generation was growing up in June. In addition the preponderance of Stage V from August till breeding begins again in the following year is plainly seen.

This sequence of events is, broadly speaking, normal for the Clyde sea area, although there may be variation in detail. A study had been made at fortnightly intervals at three other places in the area in the previous year, two of them in fairly open water and one in the deep basin (140 m) of Loch Fyne. In all these, events were much the same as in 1933; there were three distinct generations, the egg laying periods being February to March, April to May and June to July. The beginning of breeding in Loch Fyne was delayed till the middle of March and there was a varying number of small generations after the large one in July. In other years sporadic observations have confirmed these results.

The number of Stage V *Calanus* in the winter stock declines gradually and reaches a minimum at the time of first spawning. Fish indeed (1936) thinks that the greatest mortality occurs during the time between fertilization and spawning. The first generation of the year is therefore usually small in number and the maximum is usually reached with the second generation or occasionally the third.

The temperature in the Clyde sea area at the time it is homothermic in March is about 7°C; the maximum reached at the surface is in July and is about 16°C; at 30 m it is 13°C in August. In the very much colder

FIG. 29. Percentage composition of hauls of *Calanus* in Loch Striven in 1933.
A: the percentage of females bearing spermatophores; B: the succession of developmental stages through each breeding period.

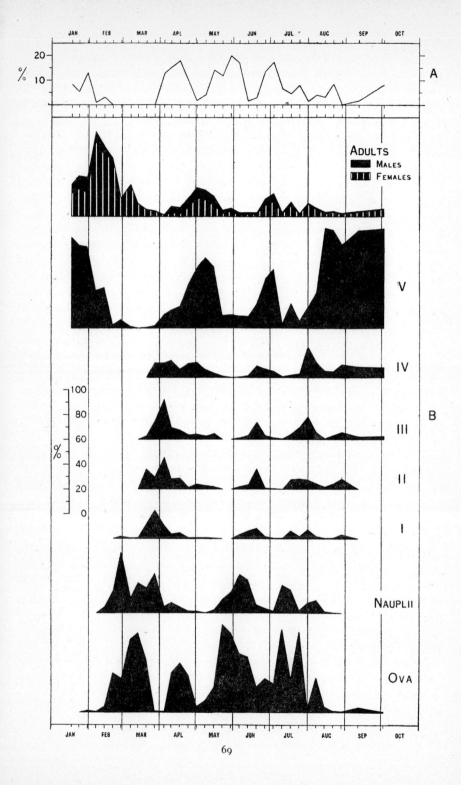

waters of the East Greenland fjords it is not to be expected that the life-
cycle can be got through so quickly and, as has already been mentioned,
there is only one generation in a year. From January to May temperature
and salinity conditions remain almost unaltered, the temperature at about
$-1.5°C$ throughout, and the salinity $32-33^0/_{00}$ at 50 m, and $27-31^0/_{00}$ at the
surface. In June the ice breaks up and a layer forms, some metres thick,
of low salinity water with a temperature at first zero, later rising a little.
Below this there is still cold Polar water with temperatures below zero
and a salinity of $30-35^0/_{00}$. In spite of the low salinity most of the *Calanus*
in summer are found living in the top 25 m. The distribution of Stages
in a series of samples taken throughout the year is shown in Fig. 30.

In autumn the stock consists of Stages III, IV and V and most of these
move down to below 50 m. The copepodites do not continue their development during the autumn but in December to January the Stage V moult
into adults, and that their fertilization takes place at this time is shown by
the large number of females carrying spermatophores. The ovaries, however, are quite undeveloped and remain so until May or June. The main
spawning takes place in July so that six months may elapse between mating
and egg laying. In the meantime, in May and June, the *Calanus* population has moved up towards the surface again, increasing greatly the
numbers above 50 m. All stages take part in this and the younger copepodites continue their development to spawn in the late summer. Whereas
there is little increase in size with the January moults from Stage V to
adult, there is a considerable growth when the younger copepodites moult,
at least after the phytoplankton increase in June.

The nauplii resulting from the July spawning are found mostly in the
surface waters with temperatures above zero and from July to September
the new generation grows up to Stage III and IV after which they sink
once more into deeper water. The adults die off in September and the
numbers decrease. It is possible that some few *Calanus* which have not
managed to reach the adult stage during the summer spend a second
winter as immature copepodites but in the main the species is annual.

The presence of males and the presence of females with spermatophores
have both been taken as signs that active breeding is going on but events
in East Greenland show that they are not necessarily so. The only safe
indication is the presence of eggs, nauplii or young copepodites.

In other regions between these two extremes the course of the life cycle
can be fitted into a similar pattern.

In the Barents Sea, in latitudes higher than those of the East Greenland
fjords investigated, *Calanus* has only one breeding period in the year. The
Calanus are found in deep water during the winter, but rise to the surface
at the end of March and spawn in April or May. The females then sink

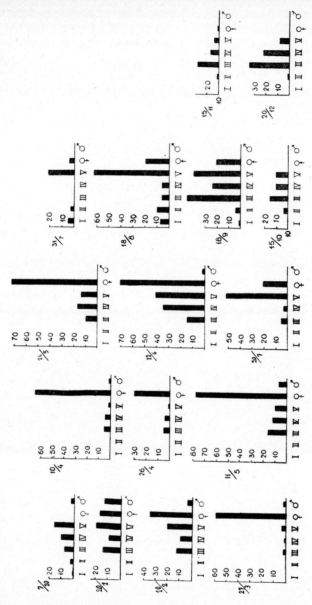

FIG. 30. Diagram showing the numbers of the copepodite stages of *Calanus finmarchicus* in ten hauls (July and August in one haul), Ella Island, East Greenland.

into deep water again where they do not long survive. When the developing copepodites have reached Stage III or IV they become bright red. They remain in the top 25 m, moving northward at the edge of the spring diatom 'flowering', but when the sea temperature begins to rise in July-August they retreat into deep water and lose their red colour. Besides this endemic population, found mainly in the northern part of the Barents Sea, there is also an influx round the North Cape from the Norwegian Sea into the southern part, which arrives in June as copepodite Stages II-V. These also are bright red in colour and, being several copepodite stages ahead of the endemic population in development, remain distinct from them until the winter.

Bogorov (1933) measured a sample of *Calanus* from the northern part of the Barents Sea and found that the females were both smaller and lighter than the males and copepodites. He suggested that they might belong to different ecological races and it seems possible that the small females belonged to the migratory, and the males and copepodites to the endemic population.

In the Lofoten area the *Calanus* in winter are found almost entirely below 200 or even 300 m, and the majority are present as Stage V although there are also some Stage IV. A migration upwards begins in mid-February and is finished by mid-March after which the great majority of the *Calanus* are found above 75 m, and most above 25 m. During the migration upwards they moult into adults and spawning occurs after that and lasts perhaps as long as 1½ months. Since Stage V of the new generation is found as early as 24th April some spawning must occur as soon as vertical migration is complete but the majority do not mature their eggs until some time later and by that time horizontal currents have carried most of the *Calanus* away from the areas where they spent the winter. This is most marked in the outer part of the Lofoten area where there are much greater water exchanges. One would expect however that these currents would also bring in *Calanus* from farther south. Sømme's observations were not continued after the end of April but by that time some of the new generation had already reached Stage V. Wiborg has shown that the spring spawning is the most important of the year but that there are later subsidiary spawnings. It is perhaps one of the generations resulting from these spawnings that migrates round the North Cape into the Barents Sea.

About 6° farther south, in the waters off Möre, the course of events is much the same although about a month earlier. A few adults can be found even in December and spawning probably begins in February. A month later conditions are complicated by an invasion from the south, varying from year to year and consisting of nauplii as well as older copepodites. This invasion may come in coastal currents travelling north or be carried in with the Gulf Stream. There is a second spawning during the summer which begins in May and June and lasts longer than the spring one.

In the Herdla and Hjelte fjords about 2° farther south *Calanus* is again found, mainly below 100 m in winter, mainly above in summer. The winter is passed in Stages IV and V, females are numerous in deep water in February, and the upward migration and spawning takes place in March. The second spawning comes late, in September-October, and after that the *Calanus* retreat to deep water. *C. helgolandicus* occurs in small numbers most of the year.

In the Oslo fjord another 2° farther south, breeding starts no earlier. There is a considerable difference between the outer and inner parts of the fjord both in hydrographic conditions and in breeding. *Calanus* passes the winter as Stage V and spawning begins in the outer fjord in March and in the inner fjord in April. Here too matters are complicated by a possible invasion of nauplii and young stages from the Skagerrak. A second spawning takes place in May (outer fjord) and July (all over). A little breeding goes on in the inner fjord in autumn and winter.

In the North Sea both *finmarchicus* and *helgolandicus* are present but although the first is more numerous it does not occur in the south western area south of about the latitude of Aberdeen, and its numbers even in the northern parts are largely dependent on immigration from the North Atlantic. There is a good deal of variation between one sub-area of the North Sea and another, but on the whole both forms show four generations in a year occurring about March, May, August and November. The late autumn generation is more marked here than elsewhere although there were signs of a small amount of breeding then at some places in the Clyde sea area. The main invasion from the north consisting of young stages takes place in July and one of later stages in August. It is the July invaders which provide the main stock breeding in the North Sea in the spring of the following year (Rees, 1949).

At Plymouth we are dealing with *helgolandicus* but the course of events is much the same as usual with a breeding period in March and another beginning in June and possibly extending through most of the summer.

Off the S.W. of Ireland also the form is *helgolandicus*. The winter is passed in Stages IV and V, moulting to adult begins in January, the males predominating then, and spawning takes place in March and goes on during April. After this reproduction seems to continue on a small scale throughout the summer. By September however over 80% of the catch is present as Stages IV and V and reproduction is over for the year.

In the western Atlantic observations have been made in the St. Lawrence and the Gulf of Maine. Filteau, in the Baie de Chaleurs, St. Lawrence, found three generations in the year. In the Gulf of Maine conditions are

F

complicated by the current system which carries the developing copepods away from the place where they have been spawned. The western part of the Gulf is earlier than the eastern and this makes the results difficult to interpret since eastern and western broods at different stages of development are circulating at the same time. However Fish has made out that in the western area spawning occurs in March to April, again in June to July and possibly also in September. In the eastern area the first spawning did not occur till May. Clarke (1940) and Clarke and Zinn (1937) have confirmed that there are two generations of *Calanus* also south of Cape Cod and, in fact, over the whole coastal area in this region.

Apart from these studies of *Calanus* for continuous periods varying from a few months to a few years, there are many scattered observations made for a short time only or during the course of expeditions. From these some further information can be obtained on the breeding of *Calanus*.

There have been numerous expeditions across the North Atlantic from Norway to Greenland and up the Davis Strait for varying distances. With (1915) has summarized the earlier of these, including Paulsen's (1906) collections round Iceland. Størmer (1929) worked on the copepods from the Michael Sars expedition and Jespersen (1934) on those from the Godthaab expedition. All these expeditions were made in summer, between May and September, so that they cover only the main breeding period.

Round the Greenland coasts there is only one generation a year, which is spawned in spring or early summer according to latitude and temperature. In the waters round Iceland however there may be a second, and even a third generation after this. Paulsen thought that the *Calanus* reproducing on the west and north coasts of Iceland had been carried there by the currents which circle round Iceland in a clock-wise direction. With (1915) however, criticized the small numbers on which some of Paulsen's results were based and thought that, although reproduction was dependent on the currents from the south raising the temperature, the *Calanus* were indigenous in the areas where the young were found.

In the Davis Strait and south of Greenland the *Calanus* are divided into two very distinct size groups, the large specimens occurring mainly in the colder water layers, whether these are deep or superficial, and the small specimens in the warmer. Størmer concluded that the large forms had sunk into deep cold water as young copepodites and had developed there slowly to a large size over a second season so that they were two years old and the small forms only one. Ussing (1938) has since shown that in cold water *Calanus* certainly develops more slowly but that, contrary to previous opinion (Gran, 1902) it grows no larger thereby but that the final size depends largely on the presence or absence of a rich food supply during the inter-moult period (see p. 83). In these northern waters there are areas where there is a rich phytoplankton production only for a limited time in early summer and others where a considerable production takes place throughout the summer (Gran, 1929; Steemann Nielsen, 1934). The size of Størmer's two groups compares well with Ussing's but more work on the relation of the large and small forms to hydrographic and phytoplankton conditions throughout the year is needed before the cause of the two size groups can be decided.

Some work in 1951 (Marshall and Orr, 1952) suggests that *Calanus* when ripe need not necessarily lay its eggs but may hold them up until conditions in the sea are favourable. The number of ripe females in the Clyde area increased in the catches from the beginning of February (see p. 79) until the beginning of March but *Calanus* eggs did not appear in the sea in numbers until the middle of March. When these ripe females were taken into the laboratory however, they almost always laid eggs overnight and the number of eggs per female increased from about 15 in January up to about 40 in the middle of March, after which it fell off. This suggests that the number of ripe eggs in the female was gradually increasing but that in the sea they were not being laid until mid-March (Fig. 31). In Tromsø Sound, North Norway, the number of eggs laid per batch also rose as the percentage of ripe females increased in the population and as diatoms increased in the plankton. Egg laying, however (see p. 66), seems usually to begin before the spring diatom increase, although the main bulk of eggs are laid after it has begun.

The population of nauplii in the sea was counted in February 1949 (Barnes and Marshall, 1951) and although there were considerable numbers of the nauplii of *Pseudocalanus, Microcalanus, Centropages, Temora, Acartia* and *Oithona* (up to 6 per l for *Microcalanus*, up to 2 per l for the rest), no *Calanus* nauplii were observed. Digby (1950) has suggested that the apparent similarity in the length of time taken for brood development in all the copepods may be not so much because the actual duration of development and maturing are the same as because they all depend on the same diatom increases. The eggs and nauplii are always present in the water but they do not grow up until there is an increase in the food supply. This may well be true for the small copepods and possibly *Calanus* shows a further specialization in that the majority refrain from laying eggs until there is a chance of their growing up. On several occasions, however, it has been observed in the sea that *Calanus* eggs were laid but from lack of food or some other cause, failed to develop, e.g. February 1933 (when the numbers were small) and April 1933 (Marshall, Nicholls and Orr, 1934). The amount of food necessary as a stimulus is not known (see, however, p. 38) and it may be considerably lower than what was called in these papers a 'diatom increase'. Diatoms usually form the increases in the food supply mentioned but this is because the minute flagellates are so much more difficult to count and nothing is known about their seasonal abundance.

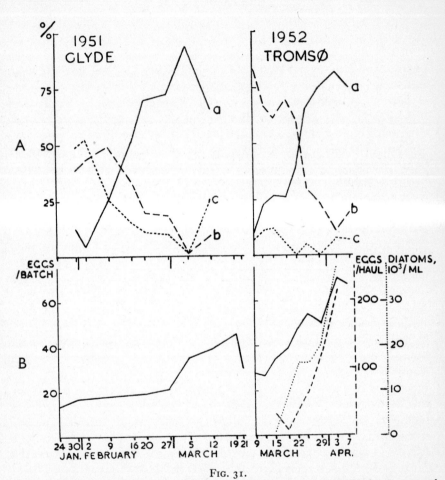

FIG. 31.

A: percentage of female *Calanus* in different states of maturity in the Clyde sea area and in Tromsø Sound: (*a*) ripe, (*b*) medium and semi-ripe, (*c*) immature. B: continuous line, average number of eggs per batch. Broken line, number of *Calanus* eggs in a 10-minute haul with a fine silk tow-net. Dotted line, number of diatom cells per ml.

In early spring the *Calanus* population keeps well in step, i.e. the majority of females become ripe about the same time and lay their eggs about the same date. In April, too, when the first generation is maturing, the majority of the females is found first in the medium state, then in the ripe. After this the generations are not so distinct and during the summer the majority of females are always ripe. This is probably because although food is much more abundant than in winter it is patchy and individual *Calanus* may vary greatly in the length of time they take to mature and in their length of life and egg laying.

INDIVIDUAL LENGTH OF LIFE

It is obvious from the foregoing that the length of life of an individual *Calanus* varies much not only from one latitude to another but also during the course of the year. The longest span, that is the length of time required to grow from egg to mature adult, plus the time which the female lives during and after spawning, is found in the far north. With possibly a few exceptions it is little more than a year. It is interesting to note that, according to Sømme the females of *C. hyperboreus* live for several months after spawning. The male is always shorter lived and even in high latitudes its life probably does not exceed seven months.

In temperate waters the greatest life span is found in the over-wintering stock. Those which moult to females may have a total life of seven to eight months.

There is considerable variation and some difference of opinion about the life span in summer in temperate waters. The observations on populations living naturally in the sea have never been made at short enough intervals to give an accurate estimate and few workers have reared *Calanus* from egg to adult. Crawshay and Allen were the first to do this and their specimens were described by Lebour (1916) who states that the experimental jars were started on 30th March 1915. 'Nauplii first appeared between the 17th and 24th of April and on 19th May Stage V was taken from the jar, having taken certainly less than two months to grow from the egg to this stage.' Two months is probably an outside estimate for this development. In the laboratory in summer most healthy eggs hatch within 24 hours (see Table II, p. 46) and those which have not hatched within 48 hours usually do not develop. The first nauplius stage lasts as a rule less than 24 hours and Nauplius III has been found as early as the third day (this is confirmed in the experiments of Raymont and Gross, 1942) though it is often later. Nauplius III is found more frequently than the other nauplius stages so that more time may be spent in this stage. Lebour noted that they were present in all her samples and Sømme says that in *C. hyperboreus* Nauplius III lasts longer than the others. If we take Lebour's first nauplii (between 17th and 24th April) as Nauplius I and add four days for the length of life of Stage V we see that her *Calanus* took about five weeks for complete development, a figure which agrees well with Nicholls' (1933a) estimate. He kept a number of *Calanus* through at least two moults each, added together the minimum time for each stage and got a total of 27 days from egg to adult. It will perhaps be interesting to go more fully into the unpublished details of these experiments. They were done in summer, June to August, and the *Calanus* were kept singly in 250 ml beakers standing in tanks with circulating water, the temperature being 14-15°C on the few occasions it was taken. The water was changed daily to provide food and the *Calanus* were removed almost daily for measurement. The results are shown in Table VI.

TABLE VI

MOULTING TIMES IN *CALANUS*

Date of capture	No.	Egg-C I	C I-C II	C II-C III	C III-C IV	C IV-C V	C V-C VI
16th June	1	—	—	—	8	13	1-4
,, ,,	2	—	—	3†	9	5	11-13
,, ,,	3	—	—	2†	4†	5	19†
,, ,,	4	—	3†	—	—	—	—
,, ,,	5	—	—	2†	10-11	3-4	11-13
29th ,,	6	—	4†	—	—	—	—
,, ,,	8	—	—	4†	6	6	5
,, ,,	9	—	—	4†	7-11	6	4
,, ,,	14	—	—	—	1†	6	14
,, ,,	20	13	—	—	—	—	—
,, ,,	20a	—	4	4	3	3	4
,, ,,	20b	—	5	3	3	3	7
,, ,,	20c	—	3	3	3	3	4
19th August	25	11*	—	—	—	—	—

* 9 days from Nauplius III to Copepodite I, and probably 2-3 days from egg to Nauplius III.

† These are minimum figures, since both moults were not seen.

The most remarkable family was that from a female (No. 20) with well developed ovaries brought in on 29th June. Eggs were laid the following day and Nauplius I was present the day after. Nauplius II appeared on 3rd July and Nauplius III on 7th June. The beaker was not examined on the 11th or 12th and Nauplius VI was first seen on 13th July along with a copepodite I. Another copepodite I appeared the following day and a third on the 16th. These three (20 *a*, *b*, and *c*) all grew up to adult females taking, from the egg, 31, 35 and 32 days respectively. The other copepodites were brought in at varying copepodite stages and followed through one or more moults. Most of them took longer than the family of No. 20, but not much longer. It is clear that there is much individual variation and a tendency to stay longer in Stage V than in any other. With 30 days as a minimum for development and about the same time for ripening the genital products, a total life of 60-70 days agrees well with the estimates from elsewhere, e.g. three months off the Norwegian coast

(Ruud, 1929), 71-79 days in the Gulf of Maine (Fish, 1936), 70-80 days in the North Sea (Rees, 1949), and 42 days from egg to copepodite Stage V in the Lofoten area (Sømme, 1934).

Rees has criticized Nicholls' estimates and points out that if the totals of each stage caught during the year are added separately the numbers rise consistently from the younger to the older, which, considering the natural mortality which must take place, indicates that the length of time in each stage increases from the first to the last. We know of course that taken over the whole year, more time is spent in Stages IV, V and VI, in the first two because of the autumn and winter delay in moulting and in the adult because of the time required to ripen the genital products. Dr D. T. Gauld has calculated the proportionate time spent in each stage by adding the total numbers of each caught at Nicholls' stations during the breeding period only (February to mid-August), and taking the number of Stage I as unity. The figures are:

Stages		I-II	II-III	III-IV	IV-V	V-VI
Proportionate time	-	1	1·53	1·69	1·95	5·59
Days - - -	-	2	3	3	3½	10½

Fitting these into the 22 days in which the laboratory *Calanus* grew from I to VI, the number of days spent in each stage is given in the bottom row and it can be seen to agree fairly closely with laboratory experiments.

Because of the time required for ripening, the females must be at almost their minimum number when the eggs are laid. The proportion dying off before egg laying probably varies in different conditions but Fish, as already mentioned, thinks that this period is the most vulnerable of the whole life cycle. The actual length of time it lasts varies during the course of the year according to the amount of food available and laboratory observations show that it may sometimes be reduced to a day or two only (see p. 34).

Nicholls' estimate of about a month is confirmed for the early part of the year by observations made on the females at Millport in 1951. All females caught in February and March were examined for their state of maturity. By the beginning of February most of the population consisted of females and on 1st February 53% of them were immature and only 4% ripe but the proportion of ripe gradually increased until on 5th March 1% was immature and 94% ripe. The sequence of events in northern Norway is similar (Fig. 31).

When a developing brood moults to adult the males appear before the females and this presumably means that their development time is slightly shorter as well as their length of life. Since it is usually impossible to distinguish the sexes before they are adult nothing is known about their relative numbers before this. The proportion of males to females caught is low and varies from place to place (Gibbons, 1936; Rees, 1949). This does not necessarily mean however that fewer are actually hatched. Results from other copepods (Marshall, 1949) have shown that even where males are scarce as adults the sexes are approximately equal in the copepodite stages (see also p. 88).

CHAPTER VI

SIZE, WEIGHT AND CHEMICAL COMPOSITION

Size

THE measurement of copepods has been made by different people in different ways. The length of the metasome is perhaps the measurement used most frequently but often the total length, i.e. to the end of the caudal furcae, has been taken. This however has the disadvantage that if, as frequently happens, the urosome is bent, two measurements are necessary. Sømme (1934) points out that after fixation a variable amount of stretching or telescoping takes place between the free segments of the metasome and especially between the metasome and urosome and that a more reliable measurement is that of the cephalosome. By this means only could he distinguish between the early copepodite stages of *C. finmarchicus* and *C. hyperboreus*. Although this is probably an improvement on the other measurements used, his suggestion has not been generally adopted. In addition different fixatives may cause either stretching or shrinking; formalin for instance increases the length slightly.

The total length of adult *C. finmarchicus* varies from 2·7-5·4 mm. Even in a single locality a great variation may be found, e.g. 3·2-5·4 mm in the Greenland Sea (With, 1915). The relative proportions of metasome and urosome also vary. According to Giesbrecht (1892) the urosome may be from $\frac{2}{7}$ to about $\frac{1}{3}$ the length of the metasome; according to Sars it is about half (see p. 5).

It has long been known that the same species of copepod is larger in the cold water part of its range than in the warm, and it was also pointed out by some observers (Gran, 1902, for *Calanus* and Kraefft, 1910, for *Paracalanus*) that the size of a copepod may vary during the course of the year. Adler and Jespersen (1920) were, however, the first to undertake a regular series of weekly measurements throughout the course of one or more years and of the three species they chose, *Calanus finmarchicus* was one. They measured adult females and copepodite Stages V, IV, III and II and although the numbers were rather small it was quite clear that, in *Calanus* as in the other species investigated, there was a distinct variation in size throughout the year, specimens being largest in spring and smallest in autumn and winter. They discussed the possible cause of this variation and came to the conclusion that temperature was the most likely. The correlation of large size with low temperature fitted in well with what was known of the varying size in different latitudes.

After this pioneer work many measurements of *Calanus* were made over part or the whole of a year and in the areas covered by numerous expeditions. Only a few of these need be mentioned. It was mostly taken for granted that temperature was the main, if not the only, cause of the size variations. One of the most interesting sets of observations are those of Størmer (1929) taken in the Davis Strait and round the south of Greenland. He found two very distinct size groups in *C. finmarchicus*, Stage V and females, the two modes in Stage V occurring at 2·7 and 3·55 mm (length of metasome). He related size to temperature and, assuming that slow development led to large size (see p. 74) put forward the hypothesis that the smaller size group had taken one, and the larger two years to develop. Subsequent workers in these far northern waters including Bogorov (1933) in the Barents Sea all found these two distinct size groups.

Marshall (1933) and Marshall, Nicholls and Orr (1934) measured *Calanus*, both adults and younger copepodites, throughout most of a year at several stations in the Clyde sea area. In all cases where a sufficient number for measurements was available, the copepods of the first generation of the year, appearing in March or April, were the largest, and those of the late summer generations the smallest (Fig. 32). The curve between the highest and lowest points was not, however, a regular one but showed subsidiary increases and decreases which seemed to be related to the breeding periods. At one station in 1932 the first of a new generation were large and the size thereafter diminished; at the other stations and in 1933 the decrease in size towards the end of a breeding period was marked, but not the increase at the beginning. Indeed in the first and most clearly defined generation in 1933 the copepods first increased and then decreased in size. This has been confirmed by the measurements of Rees (1949) in the North Sea. The minor fluctuations in size also coincided frequently with diatom increases and it was suggested that food, as well as temperature and breeding might have an effect upon size.

Russell (1928b) and Bogorov (1934) in the English Channel noted the different sizes of different generations and thought that the difference in size during the year and also from year to year depended on the temperature.

Clarke and Zinn (1937) working on *Calanus* from off Woods Hole found that, although Stages V and IV varied little in size throughout the year and were slightly larger from January to May, the adults, both male and female, showed a sharp drop in size in May with the appearance of the first generation, although these were spawned at a temperature about 6 °C lower than the adults maturing in January. This is a complete reversal of the usual relationship and is as yet unexplained. They state that food in the form of small flagellates was abundant all year and that although no diatom increase was observed, one may have been missed in February.

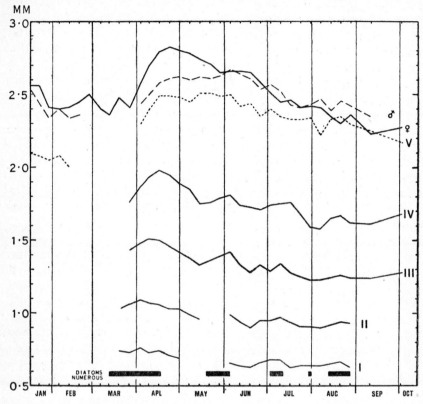

FIG. 32. The median length of the copepodite stages of *Calanus* in Loch Striven in 1933.

An important step forward was made by Ussing (1938), working in the East Greenland fjords. Like Størmer he found two size groups in cope-podite Stages IV, V, and VI. The large size group was, however, most abundant in the summer when temperature was at its highest and Ussing thought that the variations in size could be wholly accounted for by the size before moulting and the presence or absence then of phytoplankton. In this region there is only one phytoplankton increase in the year, begin-ning in June and reaching its maximum then. In July and August a small number of diatoms is present, in September they decrease markedly and are found only occasionally in October.

Since *Calanus* in the East Greenland fjords begins to reproduce in June and development reaches copepodite Stage II before September, all specimens of Stages I and II are well fed and much the same size. Stage II moults into Stage III in the course of October and although the copepodites produced later have been less well fed than the earlier ones and are rather smaller, there is still little variation in size. The copepodites produced earliest may reach Stage IV or even Stage V during the autumn and these, since they have benefited by the earlier and richer food supply, will be large. Those moulting from the later-produced and less well fed Stage III will be small; the same is true of early and late moulting Stage IV. The large Stages IV and V present in autumn either moult into adults (presumably small because there is no food to cause an increase in size) or die off during the late autumn or winter with the result that all Stages IV and V of the winter population are small. Not until the following June when the phytoplankton reappears is there an increase in the size. Those Stage III which have survived the winter feed well and moult into large Stage IV and (in July) Stage V. Since the females first appear and are mated in December-January and then live till July without reproducing, both large and small forms are present most of the year. The small forms are predominant from February to June and the large in July and August. The numbers with which Ussing dealt were unfortunately small. From his explanation it is not clear why there should be such distinct size groups; one would rather expect a gradation between the early and late developing forms.

Except in the surface layers the temperature in the East Greenland fjords varies little throughout the year but is warmest in summer when phytoplankton is abundant and copepods large. It can therefore be ruled out as a factor in the seasonal size variations. In most of the other areas where size variation has been studied, food and temperature would produce their effects simultaneously, the main diatom increase being when the sea is at its coldest, so that their separate influences would be hard to disentangle. In 1932, however (Marshall, 1933), small *Calanus* developed during a diatom increase and large during a period of diatom poverty. It should also be pointed out that Jespersen (1934, 1939*a* and *b*) found the two size groups in *Calanus* in East Greenland and other northern waters and has correlated them closely with the temperature of the water in which they were living. Wiborg (1954) when measuring *Calanus* from the west coast of Norway sometimes found two size groups but attributed this to a mixture of *Calanus* from different areas. Russell (1928*b*) also showed difference in different years in line with temperature. Ussing's work shows, however, that the effect of food has not been sufficiently taken into account.

Some very interesting experiments were made by Coker (1933) on rearing the fresh water copepod *Cyclops* in water of different temperatures and in different food concentrations. He found that temperature had a direct effect upon size, those reared in cold being larger than those reared in warm water. Lack of food on the other hand, delayed development but had no direct effect on size.

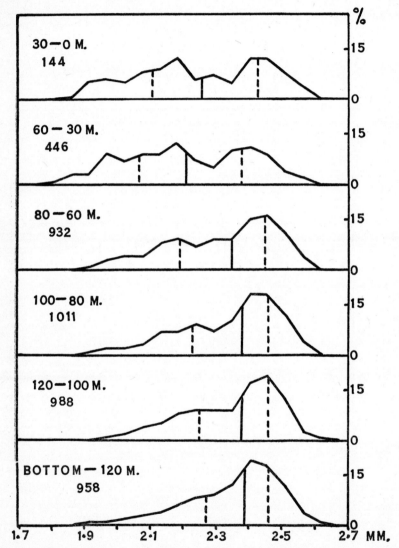

FIG. 33. The percentage size-distribution of *Calanus* from different depths in the Clyde area in January 1932. The position of the first and third quartiles is marked with vertical broken lines and that of the median with a continuous vertical line. The numbers measured for each depth are given below the depth.

In addition to the size variation with season and latitude there is a size variation with depth. It has been found both in the North Sea (Gardiner, 1933) and in the Clyde area (Loch Fyne) that, in a presumably homogeneous population, the *Calanus* which occur in the deep layers are larger than those near the surface. This has been found often too in measurements of *Calanus* taken on expeditions (Størmer, Jespersen) where it cannot be assumed that the population is homogeneous. In the North Sea the samples were taken by plankton indicator at the surface (3-8 fathoms), mid-water (9-18 fathoms), and bottom (20-35 fathoms) and Stage V was the only stage investigated although the impression was formed that the same size relations held for adults. The average size (total length) of Stage V from the surface hauls was 2·76 mm (483 specimens); from mid-water hauls 2·82 mm (409 specimens); and from bottom hauls 2·94 mm (551 specimens).

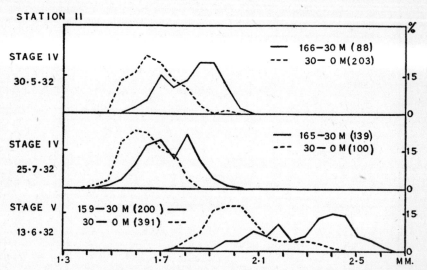

FIG. 34. A comparison of the percentage size distribution of Stage IV and Stage V *Calanus* caught above and below 30 m in the Clyde area. The numbers for each haul are given in brackets.

The measurements in Loch Fyne were confined to Stages IV and V since only these were present in sufficient numbers and the results are shown in Figs. 33 and 34. The first shows the percentage size distribution of Stage V (length of metasome), at a series of depths between about 130 m and the surface in January when the *Calanus* would all belong to the over-wintering stock, and the second the percentage size distribution above and below 30 m at one position in summer in more open water in the Clyde area.

Until it has reached Stage IV, *Calanus* does not carry out diurnal vertical migration but lives near the surface (Nicholls, 1933*b*) and from Stage IV to adult its daily migrations carry it through layers of varying temperature so that it is difficult to believe that the size differences are caused by the lower temperature of the deep water. Gardiner suggests that one factor may be the mechanical effect of the larger *Calanus* sinking more quickly and supports this suggestion by experiments showing a greater sinking rate of anaesthetized large *Calanus* than small. Jespersen (1939*a* and *b*) however finds that where a layer of cold water overlies a layer of warmer water the proportion of small *Calanus* is higher in the warm water than in the cold.

One of the most striking features of the size distribution curves for *Calanus* is the irregularity and the long range of sizes in every sample, a range almost as great as the whole yearly variation. Even when a large number of specimens are measured the curve does not lose its characteristic irregularity. Although there is rarely any suggestion of two separate modes an irregular curve might be caused by the presence of two or more distinct forms whose sizes overlap.

From work on copepods in fresh water (Gurney, 1929) and brackish water (Sewell, 1912, 1929, 1932) it has been suggested that there may be either a moult in the adult stage (Gurney) or that two forms of adult may be produced from Stages III, IV or V by moulting with appropriate growth factors (i.e. the proportion by which the length increases from one moult to the next) (Sewell). The long size range and the fact that the range for adults overlaps that for Stage V, and sometimes partly that for Stage IV also, makes either suggestion a possibility. There might be two moults in Stage V or VI or some Stage IV might moult directly into adult, with a growth factor perfectly normal for copepods. However if this kind of moult is as frequent as the size curves suggest one would expect to find it in a fairly large percentage of cases whereas, although a large number of moulting *Calanus* have been observed no such abnormal moult has yet been described.

Currie (1918) worked on *C. finmarchicus* from Canadian waters. She measured the length of Stages IV and V and also counted the number of coxal teeth in these stages. Both series of measurements gave bimodal curves but on following individual specimens through the moult she concluded that there was no second moult, and that the differences were not sexual. She suggested that two 'races' were present.

Bogorov (1933) as already mentioned found two size groups among his *Calanus* from the Barents Sea. Stages I-III were unimodal but Stages IV and V were bimodal and he suggested that this was owing to the sex differentiation taking place in Stage III.

Barnes and Barnes (1953) working in the Clyde sea area made a number of different measurements on a sample of Stage V and VI *Calanus* (both male and female) from a population which was known to be homogeneous as regards brood. On several of the measurements, the most important of which were the length of cephalosome (i.e. head +first thoracic somite), the dorso-ventral width of the urosome somites and the pointedness of the head, the Stage V population could be divided statistically into two approximately equal groups. In one group the mean measurements approximated to those of adult males, in the other to those of adult females. It seems therefore that there is in *Calanus*, as in other copepods, a size differentiation in Stage V but that the differences are population differences and the two groups overlap so much that it is impossible to identify any particular copepod as of one sex or the other. This is borne out by the fact that, of a small number of large and small Stage V watched through moult (Marshall, 1933) some of the large became male and some of the small female.

The curling of the antennules on fixation, found in most Stage V and females, but not in males, has (Jepps, 1937a) been taken as indicating sex, but Barnes and Barnes found that this was not so.

The growth factor varies much from one individual to another as well as from one stage to another as Gurney has pointed out for other copepods. The *Calanus* kept for studying rate of development (see p. 78) were measured also and the growth factors calculated. The average was: Stage I-II (one specimen) 1·22; Stage II-III (seven specimens) 1·22; Stage III-IV (thirteen specimens) 1·19; Stage IV-V (thirteen specimens) 1·17; Stage V-VI female (eleven specimens) 1·12 (range 1·06-1·21).

Rees has pointed out that his *helgolandicus* is, in the North Sea, usually larger than *finmarchicus* and some of the long range of sizes may be accounted for by a mixture of the two forms. It is a possibility which will have to be taken into account in areas where the two are likely to be found together. The fact that *helgolandicus*, which is the warm water form, is, over at least part of its range, larger than *finmarchicus* is in itself surprising (see pp. 6-7). The *finmarchicus* in the North Sea are, however, smaller than those in the Clyde sea area (Wimpenny, 1937; Rees, 1949).

It is obvious that the conditions governing size variation in *Calanus* are complicated and that the effects of the different factors are not easy to disentangle. Temperature and food are both important and it is possible that the reproductive cycle may have an influence also.

The volume of plankton animals is difficult to estimate and measurements are scarce. For *Calanus* it will obviously depend on the developmental stage, the season, and the latitude. The following figures from Gunther (1934) are a rough guide for the numbers of different stages of *Calanus* giving a volume of 1 ml.

TABLE VIIA

Numbers examined	Stage	Total length in mm	Number per ml
64	Male	3	830
94	Female	3·1	658
23	V	2·83	1125
49	V	2·48	1816
37	IV	2·1	3243
26	III	1·65	7078
24	II	1·25	14880
27	I	0·94	24900
21	Nauplii	0·585	70960

Recently Wiborg (1954) has compared the volume of different stages of *Calanus* from two places off the west coast of Norway. He measured the length and diameter of the metasome and took the volume as a cylinder. In Table VIIB are shown his figures, taking Stage V as the standard, in comparison with those calculated from Gunther. The agreement is surprisingly close.

TABLE VIIB

Stage	Wiborg		Gunther
	Ona 62°N	Skrova 68°N	Irish Sea 54°N
♂	} 160	} 160	177
♀			224
V	100	100	100
IV	49	40	45
III	17	14	21
II	6	5	10
I	2	2	6
N	0·5	0·5	3

WEIGHT

The weight and composition of the late copepodite stages of *Calanus* have been investigated chiefly by Bogorov (1933, 1934) in the Barents Sea and English Channel and by Orr (1934) and Marshall, Nicholls and Orr (1934) in the Clyde sea area. Bogorov measured the wet and dry weights of specimens which had been preserved in formalin while the other authors measured the dry weight of fresh specimens. On preservation *Calanus* readily loses part of the bolster of fat which is usually prominent along its gut and some of the differences between the results of the different authors may be explained by such loss.

It is difficult to obtain reliable estimates of the fresh weight of *Calanus*. As Bogorov has pointed out, the usual method of drying on filter paper depends very much on the individual error and on the conditions of

G

weighing. By washing the surface of the *Calanus* with a small quantity of alcohol followed by ether, he developed a method with a range of fluctuation smaller than that obtained by drying with filter paper. The liquid washing method gives only approximate results since the total removal of the external water with its dissolved salts is impossible without the loss of some internal water. Nevertheless his wet weight results, even though on formalin-preserved material, are valuable for comparative purposes. Over the year he found the average water content of females to be 78%, of males 76%, and of Stage V 65%. The water content was highest in winter and fell in spring; during the rest of the year it was fairly constant in males and females but was irregular in Stage V. A few estimations of water content in fresh specimens from the Clyde area dried rapidly on absorbent paper gave results somewhat lower than those from the English Channel. The water content was 68-70% for females, 54% for males, and 47-50% for Stage V.

For the eggs and nauplius stages no data are available but Bogorov (1933) has given them for the early copepodite stages. According to him one Stage V *Calanus* is equal in dry weight to 1·8 Stage IV, or 11 Stage III, or 42 Stage II, or 60 Stage I. Doubtless these figures are only approximate since it is highly probable that, as with males, females and Stage V, there will be seasonal changes in weight as well as differences in different latitudes.

The seasonal changes in weight of male, female and Stage V *Calanus* of the Clyde sea area are shown in Fig. 35A. During the autumn and winter when diatoms are scarce there is a general fall in weight. It seems probable that during this period they are living in part on their reserves. The lowest values are reached during the period from January to March when they may be as little as a third of their maximum for the year. With the appearance of the first generation of the year in April there is a spectacular increase in size and weight. This follows immediately after the spring diatom increase and most of the weight increase should be attributed to the good feeding conditions. The greatest increase is shown in the Stage V *Calanus* which for the rest of the year weigh more than either males or females though they show one or two violent fluctuations. These may have been caused by inadequate sampling when they were scarce. Males are the next heaviest and females lightest. At this time males or females weighed about 0·28 mg and Stage V about 0·37 mg each.

The curves for the weight of male, female and Stage V *Calanus* show a series of peaks which agree closely with the size changes in *Calanus* (Figs. 35B) and both correspond (see p. 83) with the presence of numerous diatoms in the sea at these times. The agreement is most marked for females, less so for males and Stage V. Thus after the maximum for the year is reached following the spring diatom increase in April, there are peaks early in June and in July agreeing with diatom increases at that time. After June there is a definite fall in the curves, interrupted by minor peaks

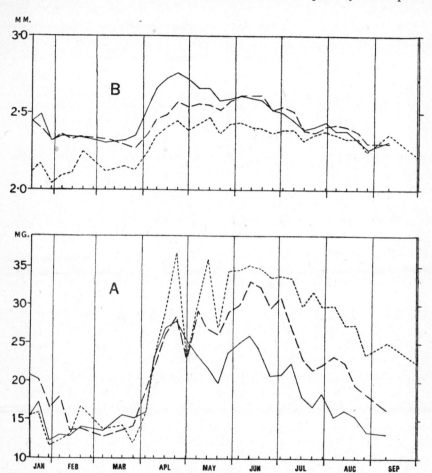

Fig. 35. Changes in median length and dry weight of 100 *Calanus* during the year 1933 in the Clyde area.
A, dry weight; B, median length; — — — male; ———— female; ------ Stage V.

which may be related to diatom increases, and this continues until the low winter values are reached again.

It is important to note that though the females are largest they are also the lightest and Stage V though the smallest are (except during the winter) the heaviest; the males occupy a middle position. This means that the relation between size and weight is very different in different stages of

Calanus. In one sample (July, 1932) the average size of 100 females was 2·39 mm and the total weight 11·3 mg; 100 Stage V at the same time measured only 2·24 mm, yet weighed 22·2 mg. It should be noted that the weights referred to above are all dry weights and the same results do not hold if we allow for the differences in water content. Thus in the living state females actually weigh more than males, and males more than Stage V. Since a large part of the difference in dry weight is accounted for by the greater fat content of Stage V *Calanus*, females have a higher specific gravity than Stage V and, as Gardiner (1933) has shown, sink more quickly.

In general the results of Bogorov in the English Channel are similar although there the *Calanus* are *helgolandicus* (Russell, 1951). There is the same autumn and winter fall to low values and the same spectacular increase during April with the growing up of the first generation for the year. Thereafter there is a less marked peak for a second generation in the summer and a still less marked autumn peak. As in the Clyde sea area there is a close agreement between size and weight, and again females are largest and Stage V smallest. Contrary to what occurs in the Clyde sea area, Bogorov in the Channel found females usually heaviest and Stage V lightest. As mentioned above the cause of the discrepancy may be that he weighed preserved specimens. *Calanus* readily loses some of its fat and since Stage V is rich in fat it would then show the greatest loss.

The weight as well as the size of many marine animals tends to increase with decrease in temperature. This is true also of plankton animals. *Calanus finmarchicus* from the Barents Sea has an average dry weight of 0·67 mg as against an average dry weight of 0·19 mg in the English Channel. The *Calanus* in the Barents Sea however produce only one generation in the year (Bogorov, 1934; Manteufel, 1941) whereas in the English Channel there are at least three.

In spite of this, however, the sum of the average dry weight of average individuals of three generations (although there may be more) at Plymouth (0·574 mg) is actually a little lower than that of the individuals of the single generation in the Arctic (0·67 mg).

Bogorov showed that in the English Channel there was a correlation between the temperature and the size and weight of the individuals in each generation; at the lower temperatures the individuals were larger and heavier, and at the higher temperatures smaller and lighter.

CHEMICAL COMPOSITION

As already mentioned the fat in *Calanus* is contained in an oil sac which lies along the gut. It is common to find in a jar containing *Calanus* that there are many oil globules on the surface. When a *Calanus* is slightly damaged globules of oil may escape from it but in spite of this it continues to live and apparently can do so for a long period. Although the oil sac is usually colourless or at most a faint pink there are times when the colour is much intensified and swarms of *Calanus* may have a pink tinge so marked as to give rise to the Norwegian name 'rød-aate'. Russian workers too recognize a definite season in the Barents Sea when red *Calanus* appear on the surface. Whether the red colour depends on the presence in the water of an abundance of diatoms or a special food, is not known.

The nature of the fat in *Calanus* has been investigated by Lovern (1935). He used for his analysis about 200 gm of fat from a pure townetting of *Calanus* from Loch Sunart. He found that the fat had a saponification equivalent of 457·5, an iodine value of 177·6 and that only 32% of the fat was saponifiable. Of the saturated fatty acids present 8·3% were C_{14}, 10·6% C_{16} and 1·3% C_{18}. For the unsaturated acids there were 1·6% of C_{14} acids, 11·8% of C_{16}, 16·8% of C_{18}, 24·5% of C_{20} and 25·1% of C_{22}. Unsaponifiable fats were not examined in detail but these differences suggest the presence of wax alcohol as found by Collin, Drummond, Hilditch and Gunther (1934) in hauls rich in *Calanus*.

The fats from *Calanus* are very different from those of fresh water plankton and correspond closely to those found in marine fish. The similarity suggests that marine fish simply deposit the fat from the zooplankton largely unchanged so that the whole character of the fats of pelagic fish is akin to that of the zooplankton. Lovern has suggested that the nature of the fat in *Calanus* may in turn depend on the fats in the phytoplankton and the red colour in Arctic *Calanus* may come from this also.

The specific gravity of the fat is given by Klem (1932) as 0·910 which would lead one to expect that the fat Stage V *Calanus* would have a lower specific gravity than adults. Though it has been observed that they sink more slowly, they are not always found nearer the surface.

There is a great variation in the size of the oil sac in different individuals and at different times of the year and this will contribute towards the seasonal weight changes. In females the water content is at its maximum in the winter and at its minimum in the spring which is just the reverse of the changes in the oil sac.

The seasonal change in the fat content of *Calanus* from the Clyde sea area is shown in Fig. 36. With the appearance in April of the first generation there was a rapid increase in fat up to 28% in females and 43% in Stage V; males were intermediate. Thereafter the curves showed a general agreement with those for weight and size. In male and female *Calanus* the three generations in the year can be distinguished by the change in fat content. In Stage V the sampling errors may sometimes have been significant and the curve for fat followed that for weight and was irregular in spring. Both the actual content and the percentage of fat are lowest for females and highest for Stage V in agreement with the weight. The lower values in females can be accounted for by the loss of fat in egg production (see p. 36). There is a maximum fluctuation in the percentage of fat in male and Stage V *Calanus* of 20% and in females of 13%. The curves show too that the large increase in the fat content in April depends chiefly on the increase in weight but that the percentage of fat increases at the same time and is related to generations. This is shown most clearly for the

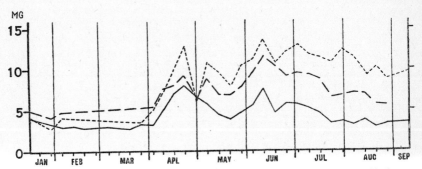

FIG. 36. Changes in fat content of *Calanus* during the year 1933 in the Clyde area. Weight of fat per 100 *Calanus*. Male, female and Stage V as in Fig. 35.

first generation of the year, less clearly for the second and still less for the third. The increases in the fat percentage suggest that the abundant food provided by the spring diatom increase results in a storage of fat. After the appearance of the third generation there is a general fall in the fat content of male and female *Calanus*, which by September have reached approximately the same values as in early spring. With Stage V, however, the value is still high in the autumn-winter stock, being about 6% higher in September than during the spring. It is obvious that at this time they are not living on their fat reserves in spite of the lack of phytoplankton. Fuller and Clarke (1936) have calculated that if *Calanus* lived entirely on its own fat it would be able to survive only for a few weeks and certainly not for several months. *Calanus* is partly carnivorous (Marshall, 1924) and possibly during the winter is able to find enough food without making inroads on its own fat reserves.

Yudanova (1940) estimated the fat content of a series of samples of plankton from the Barents Sea consisting largely of *Calanus*. The fat content had a range from 12·2-33·1% of the dry weight but since the sea-water salts were not removed these are minimal values. The early copepodite stages (II and III) had the lowest fat content and the 'red' *Calanus* which occur in abundance near the surface were the fattest. Most of the samples were taken in summer but in a sample taken in January the high value of 29% fat was obtained. She argues that the fat content must have been very high the previous autumn for them to have survived till the spring with so much of their fat reserve still retained.

The variation in the protein content of *Calanus* is shown in Fig. 37. The curve does not follow that of the weight as closely as does that of fat. Females show a gradual increase and Stage V a sudden increase with the arrival of the first generation in spring and thereafter values remain about the same level until they fall again in the autumn.

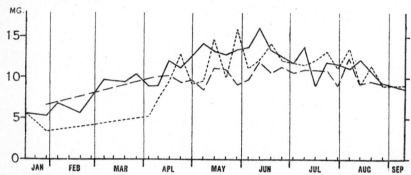

FIG. 37. Changes in protein content of *Calanus* during the year 1933 in the Clyde area. Weight of protein per 100 *Calanus*. Male, female and Stage V as in Fig. 35.

Yudanova also found that the protein content showed less variation than the fat and was independent of it.

The ash content of the winter stock of Stage V *Calanus* in the Clyde sea area is about 3·6%, and the chitin content about 3% of the dry weight.

The vitamin content of zooplankton has been investigated both because one might expect the zooplankton to be a source of the large quantities of vitamin A in the liver of whales and also because such an investigation might show whether the vitamin originates in the phytoplankton. Drummond and Gunther (1934) examined the oils from phytoplankton and zooplankton for vitamin A and D, using both chemical and biological methods of assay. Low values were obtained for zooplankton oils (predominantly from *Calanus*). A fuller investigation of the vitamin A and of the carotenoids in marine crustacea has recently been made by Fisher *et al.* 1952. They found no vitamin A in *Calanus* but as is shown in Table VIII, total carotenoids were high.

It is very puzzling that the vitamin A values for *Calanus* should be so low when the oil from other planktonic crustacea, e.g. *Meganyctiphanes norvegica* and *Thysanoessa raschii*, which are also important as whale foods, are very rich. Drummond and Gunther tested zooplankton oils (from catches in which *Calanus* was predominant) for anti-rachitic activity. Unexpectedly poor results were obtained, there being only slight curative action with large doses. This confirmed in part the results of Belloc,

TABLE VIII

OIL %, VITAMIN A AND CAROTENOIDS PER GRAM IN *CALANUS*

Date (1950)	Locality	Oil %	Total carotenoids μg/g	Total carotenoids μg/g oil	B-carotene μg/g	B-carotene μg/g oil
4 Jan.	Loch Fyne	1·6	7	420	—	Trace
4 April	Loch Fyne	2·0	18	970	0·1	7
26 June	near Norwegian coast	6·2	57	918	—	None
4 Oct.	Loch Fyne	7·9	24	331	—	None
7 Nov.	Faroe-Shetland channel	9·5	12	122	—	None

Fabre and Simonnet (1930) on the anti-rachitic properties of sterols from plankton collected at different times of the year. They too obtained poor results with mixed plankton catches taken in April and good results taken with plankton catches in July. Russell (1930*b*) has pointed out that in the English Channel *Calanus* is found early in the year in deep water where light is poor, whereas it is found near the surface in July. It is possible then that the anti-rachitic activity of the plankton in July may be caused directly by irradiation and may not depend on the phytoplankton eaten. No further work appears to have been done on this interesting problem.

CHAPTER VII

FOOD AND FEEDING

ONE of the most vexed questions in copepod biology is that of the kind and amount of food needed. The problem can be tackled in three ways. First, we can find out the food actually taken in the sea; this is a qualitative rather than a quantitative approach. Second, we can supply them with various foods and observe their intake, assuming that their behaviour is the same in the laboratory as it would be in the sea. Third, we can measure their respiration, calculate from their oxygen requirements the food necessary, and compare this with what is available in the sea. Until we know more both of copepod digestion and of the chemical composition of the food, this last method cannot take us very far. One of the difficulties has been that the three methods give divergent results. There often does not seem to be enough food in the sea to support all the copepods there.

No discussion on feeding in copepods would be complete without mentioning Pütter's hypothesis. It was he who first suggested (1907a and b, 1909, 1922, 1923, 1924-5) that there was not enough particulate food in the sea to supply the needs of the zooplankton or indeed of marine animals in general, and that they depended rather on the absorption of dissolved organic matter through their surfaces. His estimations both of the amount of dissolved organic matter in the sea and of the amount of oxygen used by copepods were much too high and his figures were later discredited. He calculated for instance that a *Calanus* needed 15,800 of the large diatom *Coscinodiscus* or 9,750,000 *Thalassiosira nana* daily to sustain itself. It was, however, very difficult to find out whether any dissolved matter at all was taken up and it was not till 1931 that Krogh showed clearly that it was negligible in amount. The discrepancy between the food needed and the food available has to be explained some other way.

FEEDING MECHANISM

Esterly (1916) first studied the process of feeding in living *Calanus*. He describes how food particles are carried into and along a funnel formed by the maxillary setae until they reach the mouth where they form into a pellet. They are held there by the stout bristles on the maxillular gnathobase until they are sucked into the mouth by a dilatation of the oesophagus.

He also describes how a pellet may be released, and scattered by a backward flick of the maxillae.

Cannon (1928) has given a detailed description of the movements and function of each limb during feeding, using a compressorium to hold the *Calanus* and a stroboscope to help in the analysis of the movements.

According to him *Calanus* shows several different kinds of movement (see p. 127) but when suspended quietly in the water it usually moves forward slowly, keeping up a rapid vibration (about 600 per minute) of the mouth parts, whose setae are spread out in fans extending almost half way round the body. By the vibration of the antennae, mandibular palps and distal part of the maxillules a swirl is created on each side of the swimming

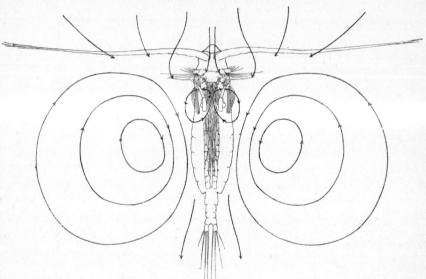

FIG. 38.   Diagram of ventral view of *Calanus finmarchicus* slowly swimming to show water currents.

Calanus with its centre about the level of the first free thoracic segment (Fig. 38); these swirls create, with the help of the movements of the maxillules and maxillipedes, smaller feeding swirls inside them, moving in the opposite direction and centred about the level of the maxillipedes. The movements of the limbs are not synchronous but each begins its back-stroke just before the limb anterior to it. The antenna and maxillipede are in almost opposite phase, but the phase difference between the mandibular palp and the maxillule is very small. The back strokes are faster than the forward strokes. The endopod of the antennae describe the greatest movement and at the end of the back-stroke their innermost setae reach the tip of the maxillules. The exopod of the antennae, the mandibular palps and the maxillules describe much smaller ellipses although the great length of the setae of the maxillular exites ensures that, although they move through the same angle, they describe a larger flattened ellipse lying against the ventro-lateral body wall. The tip of the maxillipede shows a rotary movement in an oblique plane. The maxilla shows no rhythmical movement and acts as a filter for the food particles.

The filter chamber as described by Cannon is roofed by the body wall and floored by the tips of the first one or two pairs of the forwardly directed swimming feet (Fig. 39). Its sides are formed by the maxillary setae. There is a gap between the tips of the swimming feet and the maxillary setae, which is closed anteriorly by the labrum. The only entrance to this filter chamber is posteriorly between the maxillipedes and the first pair of swimming feet. Outside it is the 'suction chamber' bounded medially by the maxillary setae and laterally by the setae of the maxillular exites. When the maxillipedes beat outwards the setae on the distal segments spread out into a fan and, moving ventrolaterally suck water into the filter chamber from behind. As the maxillipedes finish their outward stroke the maxillules, which finish their back stroke lying flat against the maxillary setae, begin to move forwards, as they do so sucking the water out of the filter chamber through the maxillary setae and trapping the food particles on them. The tips of the maxillular setae, in the course of their movement also sweep suspended particles towards the posterior end of the filter chamber. The food collected on the maxillary setae is scraped off and shoved towards the mouth by the stiff bristles on the maxillular endites or the long setae on the basal joints of the maxillipedes.

This account of the mechanism of feeding has been criticized by Lowndes (1935) who used a polygraph and cinefilm. According to him there is no metachronal rhythm and the movements of the limbs, particularly of the antennae, are much more varied than Cannon describes. They are not always in the same phase on opposite sides. The two basal segments of each antenna rotate through an angle of about 90° as well as swinging backwards and forwards. The exopod and endopod also rotate, working in opposite directions so that there is always a forward component set up. The mandibular palp has a similar though smaller, propeller-like movement. The action of the maxillules and maxillipedes is much as described by Cannon. The maxillae, though they do not move as a whole, open and close rhythmically the spaces between the setae. This description is based on *Eurytemora velox* but Lowndes says that the movements of the limbs in *Calanus* are similar but even more varied. Although he believes that filter-feeding can take place (his description of the filter chamber and the movement of water through it is similar to Cannon's) he thinks that such feeding is not automatic and that *Calanus* is mainly a selective feeder.

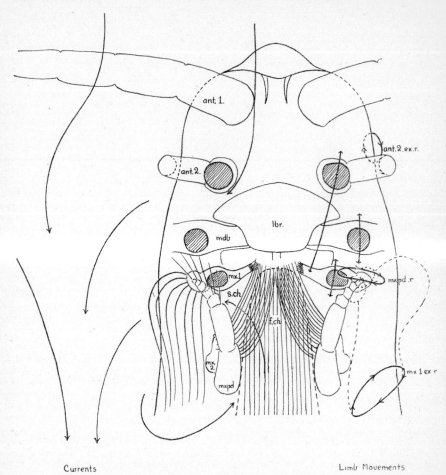

Currents   Limb Movements

FIG. 39. Diagram of anterior region of *Calanus finmarchicus*. The endopodite of the antenna, the mandibular palps and the distal parts of the maxillules have been removed. The position of the swimming trunk limbs is indicated by the shaded area inside the dotted line. On the right side of the figure the limb movements are indicated, on the left the water currents.

ant. 1, antennule; ant. 2, antenna; ant. 2 ex.r., rotation path of tip of exopod of antenna; f.ch., filter chamber; lbr., labrum; mdb., mandible; mxl., maxillule; mxl. ex.r., rotation path of tips of setae of maxillulary exite; mx2., maxilla; mxpd., maxillipede; mxpd.r., rotation path of tip of maxillipede; s.ch., suction chamber.

It is certain however that *Calanus* is for at least some of the time an automatic filter feeder. Esterly, Cannon and Lowndes have all described an efficient filtering mechanism and Esterly has watched it in use. The fact that the food in the gut (see below) during the course of the year reflects fairly accurately the microplankton present in the sea water (Marshall, 1924) and that the filtering rate is largely independent of the concentration of food in the surrounding medium (Gauld, 1951; Harvey et al., 1935), both indicate that automatic feeding can take place.

On the other hand there is a good deal of evidence that *Calanus* does not feed automatically all the time and that it is capable of some selection. A *Calanus* when kept in a culture of food organisms may remain for days swimming about actively and yet producing no faecal pellets. It is not known whether they can alter the water currents so as to avoid filtration or whether the food particles are collected as usual and scattered again by the maxillipedes. Observations at Millport have shown that often when no faecal pellets are produced in the presence of suitable foods, there is nevertheless an agglutination of the food particles which suggests that they had been filtered off and then discarded without ingestion as has been described by Esterly. The fact that crustacean remains form an important part of the gut contents indicates that the animal can capture active organisms. Harvey's experiments too (1937) on feeding *Calanus* on different species of diatom indicate that it may exert some selection and the fact that it seems rarely to eat *Ceratium* points in the same direction.

Probably *Calanus* is not confined to one method of feeding but, while usually in the course of its normal swimming movements filtering off and ingesting minute particles, it is also capable of rejecting them if unsuitable and of pursuing and capturing larger organisms when it chooses.

FOOD IN NATURE

Apart from one or two stray observations (Hensen in 1887 noted a *Cyclotella* in the gut of a copepod and Gran, 1902, saw coccoliths in copepod faecal pellets) little was known until this century about the food actually present in the gut. Then Dakin (1908) examined some *Calanus* taken in the North Sea and the Baltic and later observations were made on *Calanus* from the Californian coast (Esterly, 1916), the English Channel (Lebour, 1922) and the Clyde sea area (Marshall, 1924).

Not all *Calanus* captured in townettings contain food; the number varies both with the season and the time of day. Of over 3,000 *Calanus* examined at Millport in 1923-24, 52% contained recognizable food. This percentage varied between 20% and 70%, being 60% or over from the time of the spring diatom increase until the autumn. Apart from these, up to 30% or 40% contained an unidentifiable greenish or brownish debris. The recognizable remains were the skeletons or hard parts of the organisms eaten such as diatom frustules, radiolarian spines, peridinian cases or parts of crustacean exoskeletons. Although naked flagellates can be recognized in the gut of a freshly killed *Calanus*, they will disappear on preservation. Lebour observed *Calanus* eating large quantities of *Phaeocystis* and Marshall noted *Gymnodinium* spp., remains of *Polykrikos*, and other flagellates which were not identified.

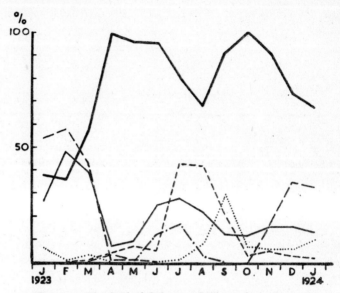

FIG. 40. The food of *Calanus* at Millport during 1923. The percentage of *Calanus* whose guts contained the following organisms: — Diatoms, — Crustaceans, — — Radiolarians, --- Dinoflagellates, ... Silicoflagellates, —·—·— Coccolithophores.

On the whole *Calanus* feed on what is common in the microplankton at the time they are caught. Fig. 40 and Table IX show the percentage of *Calanus* feeding on various types of food in the Clyde sea area in 1923 and 1924; the kind of food varies according to its abundance in the sea. Besides the organisms listed there was a small number of specimens containing algal threads, tintinnids and naked flagellates. Although silicoflagellates and coccolithophores occurred in quite a large percentage of the guts they were never there in large numbers and did not form an important part of the food. Esterly, however, found some of his *Calanus* guts packed with coccoliths. It is curious that *Ceratium* has rarely been found in the gut of *Calanus* although it is often common in the plankton. Organisms as large and much spinier can be broken up and ingested and it seems that *Calanus* must avoid this genus. Birge (1898) has noted that fresh-water copepods seldom eat *Ceratium* spp. and that an increase in its numbers is accompanied by a decrease in the number of crustacea.

At the time all this early work was done the possible importance of the μ-flagellates (those nanoplankton flagellates only a few μ in diameter) had not been recognized and they were not looked for. It is indeed improbable that they could have been recognized after ingestion. Laboratory experiments have shown (see p. 38) that they can be utilized by *Calanus* but until we know their abundance in the sea, it is impossible to assess their importance as a food.

The results of the above observations are qualitative and not quantitative for it is difficult to assess numbers when many of the organisms are broken up. Esterly mentions 29 complete coccolithophores in one specimen and 9 in another but says that in some guts there must have been a much greater number. Marshall mentions more than 60 cells of *Rhizosolenia fragillima* in many guts and a much higher number of *Skeletonema*. When the gut is packed with diatoms, however, the faecal pellets contain many cells whose contents seem unaltered and the number in the gut is not necessarily a true guide to the number digested.

Wimpenny (1937) and Gauld (1953) have both estimated the percentage of *Calanus* feeding at different times throughout the day and year. Wimpenny found the numbers higher in early spring and autumn than in summer. Females fed more freely in autumn than in early spring and Stage V more in spring than in autumn. The percentage feeding decreased steadily from Stage I up to adult with the exception of Stage V which was intermediate between females and males. This is probably accounted for by the low winter feeding rate (see p. 113).

Marshall found that in the Clyde sea area in winter *Calanus* fed almost entirely during the hours of darkness, even bright moonlight having a deterrent effect, but that in summer there was little difference between night and day. Wimpenny (1938) confirmed that they fed more at night and even in June in the North Sea found that 66% of *Calanus* were feeding near midnight as against 41% at 5 a.m.

Although Fuller (1937) obtained some evidence of a diurnal feeding rhythm with greater activity at night, Gauld in laboratory experiments did not confirm this. Gauld also made an examination of the feeding behaviour of *Calanus* in Loch Fyne, taken at several depths and at monthly intervals throughout a year, and came to the conclusion that there was no innate diurnal feeding rhythm. When vertical migration was taking place feeding was confined to the hours of darkness when the *Calanus* were at the surface. As might be expected since their food lives mainly near the surface those caught in deep water contained less food than those taken in surface waters. When the *Calanus* are at the surface all the time, feeding goes on both day and night. The observations were made chiefly on females and Stage V, and are probably true for younger stages also. Males were more

TABLE IX

Month	Guts empty %	Debris only %	Recognizable food %	Percentage of feeding Calanus whose guts contain						No. of Calanus examined	Diatoms most common
				Diatoms	Dino-flagellates	Silico-flagellates	Coccolitho-phores	Radio-laria	Crustacea		
1923											
Jan.	38	43	19	38	0	6	0	54	27	179	Coscinodiscus
Feb.	24	30	46	36	0	1	0	58	48	328	Coscinodiscus
March	27	15	58	57	1	3	0	43	39	135	Coscinodiscus, Biddulphia, Naviculids
April	28	7	65	99	4	0	4	1	7	268	Skeletonema, Thalassiosira, pennate
May	27	7	66	96	7	0	1	1	9	256	Skeletonema, Thalassiosira, pennate
June	28	9	63	95	5	0	12	0	25	241	Skeletonema, Thalassiosira, pennate
July	21	13	66	80	43	1	17	0	28	141	Rhizosolenia, Chaetoceros
August	22	16	62	68	42	8	3	0	22	120	Rhizosolenia
Sept.	21	10	69	91	21	30	0	0	13	130	Thalassiosira, Skeletonema, Chaetoceros
Oct.	28	2	70	100	3	7	0	0	12	155	Skeletonema, Thalassiosira
Nov.	31	19	50	91	5	6	0	17	16	257	Thalassiosira, Skeletonema
Dec.	41	29	30	73	3	6	0	35	16	336	Thalassiosira
1924											
Jan.	31	36	33	67	2	10	0	33	13	188	Thalassiosira, Coscinodiscus
Feb.	24	32	44	72	3	7	0	27	18	169	Thalassiosira, Coscinodiscus
March	34	7	59	91	0	5	0	13	18	91	Skeletonema, Thalassiosira
April	20	2	78	93	2	2	0	0	12	54	Skeletonema, Thalassiosira

irregular; a smaller percentage were found feeding and on the whole they contained less food.

DIGESTION

Large diatoms, radiolarians and crustacea, such as are not taken in whole, are broken up, presumably by the labral teeth and mandibles. They are then passed or sucked into the gut and are exposed to the secretions of the anterior part for some time, being moved to and fro by peristaltic contractions. The undigested food collects in the narrow posterior part of the gut in the metasome and is gradually compacted into a faecal pellet which is then ejected (Fig. 42). A delicate pellicle is seen round the pellet often forming a transparent 'tail'. This may be chitinous, as described by Forster (1953) in some decapod crustacea.

Little is known about the digestive enzymes but some experiments have been made by Bond (1934) and Hasler (1937), and at Millport, using extracts of whole animals with distilled water and glycerine (Millport), or alcohol (Bond) or extracts with glycerine from acetone-dried and ether-extracted *Calanus* (Hasler). The use of whole animals is not a very satisfactory method since the quantity of enzyme obtained is very small and is mixed with relatively large quantities of body tissues.

The results show, however, that there are present enzymes which will digest starch, gelatine, and some types of fat; for example ethyl butyrate, tributyrin and methyl acetate were attacked but there was no discernible effect on alkaline milk or olive oil. In a series of tests made at Millport sometimes positive and sometimes negative results were given for digestion of maltose, saccharose, glycogen, fibrin and calcified milk. Negative results were given with lactose, inulin, cellulose (filter paper), casein (all at Millport) and alginic acid (Bond). Bond also experimented with suspensions of several living organisms and found that after 24 to 36 hours *Nitzschia closterium*, *Dunaliella salina* and *Bacterium alginovorum* all showed signs of digestion.

An estimate of the time food remains in the gut can be obtained by timing the rate of production of faecal pellets. In rich food concentrations Harvey (1942, 1950) has found that one may be produced every 20 minutes. The speed of production of faecal pellets was measured at Millport several times by putting a *Calanus* which had been living in a food culture of one organism into a culture of another and noting the time taken for the new organism to appear in the faecal pellets. This was once as little as 15 minutes and varied from 15–37 in 6 tests at room temperature. When feeding actively in a culture, pellets were usually produced at the rate of about 6 per hour with a maximum of about 12 per hour. The rate of production falls in lower concentrations and in ultra-filtered water only one or

H

two 'ghost' pellets (small, transparent and containing nothing identifiable) (Fig. 42e) are produced in 24 hours. In the rich concentrations digestion may be only partial for when teased out the pellets can be seen to contain many apparently unattacked cells. That digestion and assimilation can be very rapid was shown by feeding female *Calanus* on cultures containing radioactive phosphorus (see p. 38).

The results as a whole show that, as one might expect, *Calanus* can digest certain types of protein, fat and carbohydrate, but to learn more it would be necessary to know the chemical composition of the foods taken, and to work with extracts of the gut only.

Respiration

The oxygen used by an animal in respiration is a measure of its energy requirements and from this can be calculated the food necessary to maintain it. With this purpose in view several workers have measured the respiration of *Calanus* and their work is dealt with in Chapter VIII.

Experimental Feeding of *Calanus*

The attempts to prove or disprove Pütter's hypothesis led to a great deal of useful work on the feeding of copepods. *Calanus* was fed on various diatoms and flagellates, first to find out what amount of these was sufficient for growth and moulting and later to find the volume of water which it could filter daily.

It was realized that bacteria and the smaller nanoplankton forms might be important and in America attention was turned first to them (Clarke and Gellis, 1935; Fuller and Clarke, 1936; Fuller, 1937; Clarke and Bonnet, 1939). At first Clarke and Gellis thought they had found a distinct improvement in survival with bacteria alone as food but later Fuller and Clarke decided that this was not so. In a carefully controlled experiment when Stage IV and V *Calanus* were kept in flowing sterile water and had bacteria or flagellates added as food, they found survival best in the sterile water although the only moults occurred in those fed. The high mortality and lack of successful moults led them to the conclusion that bacteria were not an adequate food. In any case the number present in normal sea water is much too low for them to be the only food.

Clarke and Bonnet did some further experiments on feeding Stage V with different concentrations of *Nitzschia closterium* var. *minutissima* at different temperatures and thought that the optimum concentration was somewhere between 30,000 and 1,500,000 cells/ml (the higher of these concentrations being harmful) and that although survival was best at low temperatures, growth and moulting were retarded.

Since survival and moult were much better in unfiltered water Fuller and Clarke took a sample of sea water at the time and place the *Calanus* were caught, counted all the organisms in it and calculated their nutritive content. The sample was a fairly rich one containing about 100 diatom and peridinian cells per ml. Taking the food requirements from the respiration figures of Marshall, Nicholls and Orr (1935) they then estimated at 72 ml the amount of this water which a *Calanus* would have to filter daily to maintain itself, and followed this up by measuring the actual filtering rate, using carmine particles. This turned out to be only about 5 ml per day and further estimates by Fuller (1937) using suspensions of *Nitzschia closterium* gave an even lower figure, an average of only 1·09 ml per day. The *Calanus* were kept in a very small quantity of sea water—3 in 15 ml— and this in itself must have affected the results unfavourably. He did find however that the rate of filtering was independent of the concentration of suspended cells and that *Calanus* did not necessarily feed continuously but might stop for some hours or even days. Fuller also found a diurnal rhythm in feeding, the *Calanus* taking more by night than by day (see, however, p. 103). He concluded that the *Nitzschia* used was so small as to pass through the maxillary filter (see below). Later estimations (Gauld, 1951) have shown that Fuller's values are much too low. In most of the foregoing experiments the mortality was high and the number of successful moults small and it may be that the *Calanus* were not in a very healthy condition.

Raymont and Gross (1942) kept *Calanus* in a variety of cultures of diatoms and flagellates and found that they would live well and moult and the females lay eggs. Some of the flagellates used were very small—1-3μ in diameter—and they found that survival was not so good in a pure flagellate culture as in one with some larger diatoms present. Organisms used successfully were *Nitzschia closterium* var. *minutissima*, *Skeletonema costatum*, *Chaetoceros pseudocrinitus*, *Ditylum brightwelli*, *Chlamydomonas* sp. and a variety of small flagellates. They concluded that a concentration of 200,000 *Nitzschia* cells/ml was the lower limit for successful growth and moulting, but this is a figure much above what has ever been recorded in the sea.

Harvey (1937) did four very interesting experiments on feeding *Calanus* with mixtures of diatoms kept in suspension by gentle stirring. He obtained evidence that the copepods could select one species from a mixture. For example when *Calanus* were kept in sea water to which *Ditylum* had been added and were then put in a mixture of *Ditylum* and *Lauderia borealis* (a diatom about one-third of the size of *Ditylum*) the calculated filtering rates per hour were, for *Ditylum* 10·0 ml and for *Lauderia* 2·2 ml. When the experiment was done the other way and the *Calanus* were fed first with *Lauderia* only, they still selected *Ditylum* but to a less extent; the filtering rates were then 7·0 ml/hr for *Ditylum* and 3·3 for *Lauderia*. *Calanus* fed on *Lauderia* only and then put in a mixture of *Lauderia* and *Chaetoceros* ate *Lauderia* only with a filtering rate of 2-3 ml/hr. *Calanus* kept in a mixture of *Lauderia* and *Nitzschia closterium* var. *minutissima* ate mainly *Lauderia*. The filtering rate for *Nitzschia* was very low and compared with that found by Fuller for the same species. This seems to indicate that it is not a suitable food for *Calanus* yet it was used successfully by Raymont and Gross and in Crawshay's rearing experiments (Lebour, 1916) although the variety Crawshay used is not stated. Harvey does not claim that the *Calanus* in his experiments selected the food they were accustomed to, merely that they selected one species rather than another. The rates of filtration he found for *Ditylum* are very much higher than those recorded by other workers for other species.

Harvey and Fuller both suggested that *Calanus* might be able to filter large organisms more easily than small. Gauld (1951) however has shown that high filtering rates can be maintained with organisms as small as *Chlamydomonas* sp. (diameter 6-8 μ). His methods were essentially the same as those of Fuller and his higher figures may be because his *Calanus* were kept in larger volumes of sea water and were therefore healthier. His experiments (Fig. 41) were done over 24 hour periods so the rate must be minimal. Yet he found an average of about 70 ml filtered per day (range 42-101 ml) which is the volume taken by Clarke as that necessary for a *Calanus* to maintain itself. Clarke's estimate was made when the sea was fairly rich in microplankton and it is probable that during the winter, when food in the form of phytoplankton is very scarce, they will have to filter more in spite of the reduced respiration at the lower temperatures. There is evidence, however, that Stage V *Calanus* of the over-wintering stock eat less (see p. 113) at the same temperature than the females into which they moult or than the Stage V of the first generation of the year. The figure of 70 ml is based on the assumption that the food is evenly distributed throughout the water and this is unlikely to be so in nature. The copepods occur in small swarms and it is possible that their food will do so also.

Indeed Gauld has shown (p. 103) that the guts of *Calanus* in the sea are full only during the hours they are in the phytoplankton rich upper layers. Since during the period when *Calanus* migrates vertically, it will spend only a few hours a day in the productive layers, the amount filtered would have to exceed by several times the volume of 70 ml postulated by Clarke for diatom rich water.

Further it cannot be assumed that the whole of the food represented by the phytoplankton is available to *Calanus*. In Harvey's grazing hypothesis it is assumed that during diatom rich periods the bulk of the food taken in is passed through the gut undigested. By growing cultures of different phytoplankton organisms in media containing radioactive phosphorus as a tracer element, it is possible to estimate the number of phytoplankton cells

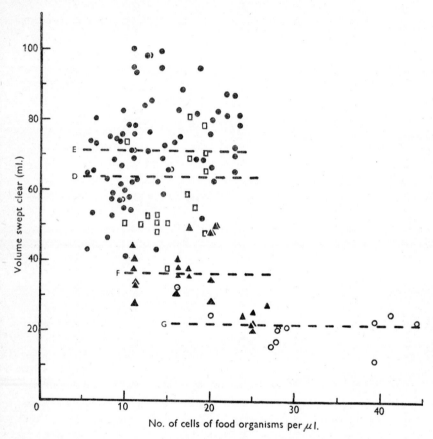

FIG. 41. Volume in ml. of cultures swept clear by *Calanus* in varying concentrations of food culture, measured as cells/μl, □ ● Stage V; ▲ Stage IV; O Stage III.

taken in by *Calanus* in the laboratory, the degree of retention of the phosphorus-containing portion and the volume filtered. These experiments have shown that for diatoms and some flagellates the percentage utilization is high—sometimes up to 90%—although for *Chlorella* and some other organisms it is low. The volume filtered in the laboratory is only a few ml in 24 hours but may occasionally rise to 20-40 ml. The apparent gap between the food available in the sea and that required by *Calanus* remains unexplained.

PRODUCTION OF FAECAL PELLETS

Harvey *et al.* (1935) counted the faecal pellets produced in the sea as a method of measuring the grazing down of the phytoplankton and later, in the laboratory, Raymont and Gross (1942) made some observations on their shape and colour when *Calanus* was fed on different foods and on the differences in those produced by males and females. Since it seemed a quick and convenient way of measuring the amount of feeding it was used at Millport for a number of experiments on the effect of different factors on feeding. The size of the pellets produced by one animal, even on a uniform diet, varies, and the number can therefore be only an approximate measure of the food eaten but, by taking a number of *Calanus* together and running the experiments in duplicate or triplicate, the averages produced were fairly consistent. The scatter of the points when plotting number of faecal pellets produced against number of food cells in the medium, is not more than that found in experiments where the uptake is measured by estimating the decrease in the number of food cells (Gauld, 1951).

Ussing (1938) suggested that the maxillary filter of an adult *Calanus* would not be fine enough to sieve out μ-flagellates, but this is not borne out by experiment. *Dicrateria inornata*, a flagellate about 3-5·5 μ in diameter was taken by all stages from copepodite Stage I to adult. Naumann (1923) has stated that calanoid copepods can filter off particles as small as 1 μ. There is also an upper size limit; some cells (see p. 112) are too large to be easily negotiated by the smallest copepodite stages. Inert matter is taken in too and formed into faecal pellets. A mixture of *Chlamydomonas* and Indian ink was taken as freely as pure *Chlamydomonas* but on the other hand, in a mixture of *Chlamydomonas* and carmine hardly any faecal pellets were formed. The pellets produced vary very much with the kind of food given. Those produced with *Chlamydomonas* as food are usually well-compacted and dark in colour; those produced with diatoms are less compacted, lighter in colour and usually larger. In those produced with peridinians the skeletons are visible inside, bulging out the pellet. Fig. 42 shows characteristic pellets produced by a number of foods.

In a series of experiments *Chlamydomonas* was taken as the standard food and the production of faecal pellets in others compared with it. Such experiments were made with cultures of cells both larger and smaller than *Chlamydomonas* and the following were found to be taken freely: *Dicrateria inornata* (one nineteenth of the volume of *Chlamydomonas*), *Pseudopedinella* (about the same volume), *Gymnodinium* sp. (about 4·3 times the volume), and *Peridinium trochoideum* (about 10 times the volume). Foods which, to judge from egg production (see p. 37) are not of much use to *Calanus* are sometimes ingested as readily as more useful organisms.

In another type of experiment the concentration of the culture was

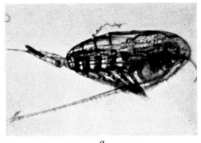

a

b

d

e

c

f

FIG. 42

(*a*) *Calanus* producing a faecal pellet,
(*b–f*) faecal pellets produced by female *Calanus* on different types of food,
(*b*) *Chlamydomonas*, (*c*) *Lauderia*, (*d*) 'ghost' pellets, (*e*) *Peridinium trochoideum*,
(*f*) the same enlarged to show the individual skeletons in the pellets.
(*b–e*) × 20, (*f*) × 80.

varied. In general the number of faecal pellets increases with increasing concentration as one would expect from the filtering rate (Gauld, 1951), but there is a limit beyond which the faecal pellet number does not increase any more. This may be caused by the filtering setae getting choked up. The results were rather variable however and it was impossible to set an actual figure for the limit of efficient filtering.

The effects of light and of temperature on the production of faecal pellets were also investigated.

Exposure to strong diffuse light is lethal (see p. 136) and the comparison was therefore made between weak diffuse light and darkness. There was no obvious difference in the number of faecal pellets produced, but when the assimilation of food was measured using radioactive phosphorus, it was decidedly lower in the light. This indicates that if *Calanus* has the power of selecting its food it does not do so by sight.

With increasing temperature the *Calanus*, as was to be expected, produced more faecal pellets but the increase was rather variable.

Food of Different Stages

Although much work has been done on the food of Stage V and adult *Calanus* little or nothing is known about the food of nauplii and early copepodites. Some observations were therefore made at Millport on the organisms which could be ingested by these early stages.

The possibility has already been mentioned (p. 53) that Nauplius I and perhaps also Nauplius II do not eat at all. When nauplii are kept in the laboratory many of them reach Nauplius III and then die. In all the nauplius stages the mouth parts differ greatly from those of the adult and they must therefore obtain their food in a different way. It is true that in Nauplii V and VI the maxillules, maxillae, and maxillipedes appear but they are undeveloped, feeble and can hardly be functional. The food must consist of small particles and, because nauplii are less mobile than the adults, it must be present in richer concentration. Since the amount which the nauplii eat is likely to be so small as to be within the experimental error of counting culture cells, the most reliable way of finding out what they have taken is by examining the faecal pellets. So far the pellets of nauplius Stages I and II have not been certainly identified and examined but those of nauplius Stages III to VI are easily recognizable in the laboratory, as are those of all copepodite stages. In its mouth parts copepodite Stage I is, but for the smaller number of setae, completely like the adult and presumably feeds in the same way.

Observations on the faecal pellets produced under experimental conditions by the developmental stages have shown that the main difference is in their size which, apart from the male, increases with each moult

(Table X). When fed on the same culture the number of pellets produced does not depend on the stage of development (again excepting the

TABLE X

AVERAGE LENGTH OF FAECAL PELLETS
OF *CALANUS* FED ON *CHLAMYDOMONAS* CULTURE

	Nauplius			Copepodite				
Stage	V and VI	I	II	III	IV	V	♀	♂
Size in μ	70	85	173	227	370	520	470*	240

*This may be an under-estimate for some of the large pellets were broken.

male) and often all stages produce approximately the same number of
faecal pellets.

In the faecal pellets of the earlier stages the organisms actually identified
were as follows:

Nauplius III to V, *Skeletonema costatum* (cells 5 μ diameter) *Syracosphaera* sp. (Millport strain 62, 20 μ long).

Nauplius VI (and V?), *Prorocentrum triestinum* (20 × 14 μ); *Peridinium
trochoideum* (25 × 19 μ).

Copepodite I. In addition to the above, *Prorocentrum micans* (43 × 27 μ),
Syracosphaera carterae, *Nitzschia closterium*, Naviculid sp. 26 μ long.

Copepodite II. In addition to the above, *Coscinodiscus centralis* (about
100 μ in diameter), *Ditylum brightwelli* (25-60 μ broad, length 2-3
times greater).

Faecal pellets were produced by copepodite Stage I kept in *Coscinodiscus*
and *Ditylum* but the diatoms could not be identified in them. With Stage
II kept in a *Coscinodiscus* culture the number of pellets containing *Coscinodiscus* was only a fraction of the total number produced. Further observations will certainly increase the number of species known to be suitable
as food. Copepodite Stages III and IV eat the same as V and adults,
whose food has already been described.

Late nauplii have evidently quite a number of foods available even if
they confine themselves to cells below 25 μ in diameter. It seems probable
that the younger nauplii will be able to eat organisms up to perhaps 10 μ
in diameter which will include the smaller diatoms as well as many
flagellates.

Raymont and Gross (1942) noted that male *Calanus* eat much less than
female and produce smaller and fewer faecal pellets. They found that
females produce two to ten times as many pellets and that the volume-
ratio of female to male pellet is 5 or 6 to 1 when they are fed on *Ditylum* or
Skeletonema and as high as 50 to 1 in one experiment when fed on *Skeletonema* and *Nitzschia*. In an experiment lasting 68 hours when males

and females were kept in equal volumes of the same *Ditylum* culture, the females by the end of that time had swept the water almost free of diatoms whereas the males still had masses of food available and yet many had empty guts. On the other hand it is possible to conclude from their results that males use more cells to make a faecal pellet and are therefore more efficient feeders.

Experiments at Millport comparing the faecal pellet production of males and females in different foods have confirmed the fact that females produce more and larger pellets. The ratio varied from 2 to 1 up to 6 to 1; the relative size (on *Chlamydomonas* as food) is shown in Table X. Even in February when the gonads of the males must have been developing actively, the number of faecal pellets produced was much lower than in females.

One further instance of differential feeding must be noted. When comparing Stage V and newly-moulted females of the over-wintering brood it was found that the Stage V produced fewer pellets than the females. On 11th January 1951 females produced an average of 43·6 in 24 hours as against 23·2 by Stage V (omitting one lot of Stage V which produced scarcely any), and on 24th January (in a richer culture of *Chlamydomonas*) females produced 71·3, males 27·8 and Stage V 18·3. On 9th April, however, when the next generation had grown up the females and Stage V were compared again and the Stage V were eating even more than the females. Females produced an average of 23·6 faecal pellets and Stage V an average of 37·6 in 24 hours.

CHAPTER VIII

RESPIRATION

INTEREST in the respiration of marine copepods has been centred chiefly in the food requirements. The first measurements recorded are these of Ostenfeld (1913) who estimated the oxygen used by adult *Calanus hyper-boreus* and found it to be 0·68 μl/*Calanus*/hour, a value which compares well with recent measurements on the smaller species, *C. finmarchicus*. Pütter (1922, 1923, 1924-25) made a long series of experiments on mixed catches of copepods which he divided into small, medium and large. They consisted mainly of the copepods *Pseudocalanus, Centropages, Paracalanus, Acartia* and *Oithona*. The methods he adopted were approximate and the probable sources of errors were considerable; they have been criticized by Krogh (1931). It was the high results Pütter obtained which confirmed him in his belief that organic matter in solution was the chief source of nutriment for marine animals. According to him *Calanus* must consume as food the equivalent of 39% of its own weight daily in summer.

If the high values obtained by Pütter were even of the correct order of magnitude it seemed that the known sources of food in the sea, diatoms, peridinians and flagellates must be insufficient for their needs. Research since then has therefore been undertaken, first to re-assess the respiration of copepods and secondly to examine the plankton to see whether other living organisms which have hitherto escaped notice are present in sufficient quantities as food for copepods.

In order to obtain more accurate figures for the respiration of *Calanus* and the effect of varying environmental factors on it, a study was made by Marshall, Nicholls and Orr (1935). For each experiment they used a considerable number of animals, usually over 100, and each respiration bottle contained about 170 ml of sea water. The estimations were made by drawing off samples and measuring the oxygen content by Winkler's well-known method. It is obvious that the *Calanus* were under far from normal conditions since for each *Calanus* there was an average of only 1-2 ml of water. This crowding and the disturbing effect of touching the glass walls may well have led to higher results than would otherwise have been obtained. The *Calanus* were not anaesthetized and Stage V *Calanus* swam about actively; males and females were usually more sluggish. Activity affects respiration considerably in animals and it would have been desirable to make the measurements under known conditions of activity. According to Zeuthen (1947) however cold-blooded animals at rest and unfed often show a gradually decreasing metabolism and never reach a well defined level. The activity of *Calanus* varies considerably under different conditions. There is for example usually a diurnal migration affected chiefly by light, there are feeding movements and there are escape movements.

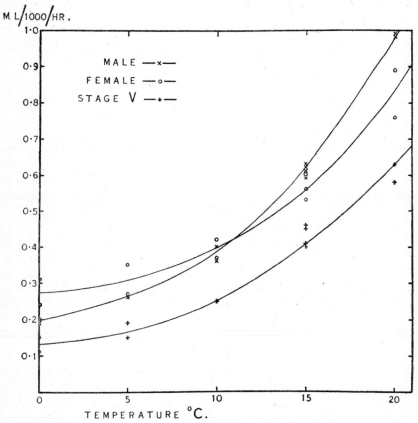

FIG. 43.   The effect of temperature on oxygen consumption.

There are also other factors affecting respiration which can, however, be controlled either wholly or in part. The time after capture may affect the respiration. Immediately after capture *Calanus* has a considerably higher respiration than some hours later. This fall is most marked in the first few hours and is not noticeable after about one day. It is most marked with females, less marked with males and not noticeable with Stage V *Calanus*. Though few observations were made there seems to be a more definite fall after capture in winter than in summer. Keys (1930) working with fish found that values for respiration were above normal for some time after putting the animal under experimental conditions. With *Calanus* the cause may be partly the disturbance of capture and picking out.

The temperature has a marked effect on the respiration of *Calanus* as is shown in Fig. 43. The oxygen consumption doubles from 0°-10°C and above this increases at a still greater rate and thus does not follow van't Hoff's law. The values for male and female *Calanus* are close and the differences between them are not significant. For Stage V *Calanus* however the values are always lower even in spite of their apparently greater activity. At 20°C the *Calanus* are close to their lethal temperature and there may be a slight harmful effect. Results similar to those shown in the figure are found at different times of the year though the variation in the oxygen consumption at 10°C may be as much as 0·2 μl per copepod per hour. The differences show no relation to size changes throughout the year (see p. 82) except that Stage V *Calanus* which are always smaller than the adults always have a lower oxygen consumption. The low values of respiration for Stage V *Calanus* are surprising since in addition to their greater activity they are in the early part of the year of about the same weight as the adults and in summer are heavier (see pp. 90-91).

No one has investigated whether there is an indirect effect of temperature on respiration in *Calanus*. If a cold-blooded animal is transferred to a lower temperature there is an immediate decrease in the respiration. With many species however after having been kept at a lower temperature for some time, the respiration rises to a higher value. Similarly when transferred from a lower to a higher temperature, their initially increased respiration falls gradually to a lower level. Fox (1937, 1939), Fox and Wingfield (1937) and Edwards and Irving (1943a and b) compared a number of animals from different latitudes and found that a given rate of heart-beat, respiratory movement or oxygen consumption occurs at a lower temperature in individuals living in a colder sea than in those from a warmer sea. Similar results have been obtained with a large number of species by other workers also. If the same holds for *Calanus* one would expect to find *Calanus* in the Arctic with values for respiration considerably greater than those shown in Fig. 43 at the same temperature, especially when the greater size of the *Calanus* in cold seas is allowed for. Riley, Stommel and Bumpus (1949) have stated that with *Calanus* there is a partial adjustment of metabolism seasonally. On the other hand the eggs of *Calanus* at Tromsø where the sea temperature in spring is 0°-3°C develop in the same time at the same temperature as in warmer waters.

Changes in hydrogen-ion concentration have been shown to be important for many aquatic animals, but even changes exceeding those normally found in the sea had no effect on the respiration of female *Calanus*.

Variations in the oxygen content of the sea may be quite large and though values much in excess of saturation are uncommon, low values may be present in deep water in localities where there is poor circulation or breakdown following intense productivity in the upper layers. It was found that at 15°C even very high values for oxygen content (up to 16 ml/l) had no effect on the oxygen consumption. When the oxygen content decreased however there was a rapid fall in respiration at about 3 ml/l at 15°C. This drop in oxygen consumption was apparently a symptom of unhealthiness as well for a number died at values of 3·3 ml/l and the death rate increased rapidly at lower oxygen contents. Male *Calanus* were the most sensitive to oxygen reduction. At about 3 ml/l or below females were slightly more resistant than males while Stage V withstood oxygen reduction to considerably lower values. At 5°C the resistance to lower oxygen content was increased and as before males and females were less resistant than Stage V. This sensitivity of *Calanus* to low oxygen content is surprising for in the sea *Calanus* may be abundant in places where the oxygen content falls as low as 2 ml/l (Marshall and Orr, 1927). *Calanus* is also recorded from the limiting depth for plankton in the Black Sea in February when the oxygen content is below 1 ml/l and the temperature is 7°C (Nikitin, 1931).

A lowering of the salinity has an effect on the respiration of *Calanus*. By reducing the salinity gradually a high percentage of experimental *Calanus* can tolerate salinities of $17^0/_{00}$. When the respiration values at salinities of $34^0/_{00}$, $27^0/_{00}$ and $17^0/_{00}$ are compared there is a reduction only at the lowest salinity from about 0·38 μl/copepod/hour to 0·25 μl/copepod/hour.

One of the most surprising facts about the respiration of *Calanus* is the increase caused by exposure to light; in bright diffuse light or in sunshine the respiration may be double what it is in the dark. The light intensity at which this increased respiration is obtained may be comparatively low for it occurs even when the *Calanus* are sheltered from direct sunlight and even on a cloudy day. On the other hand an artificial light source (e.g. a 60 w gas-filled lamp at 25 cm) or diffuse light indoors has no effect. If, after exposure to light, measurements on the respiration are continued in the dark, the values obtained are below those in dark controls suggesting that the *Calanus* have been injured.

Since light under natural conditions in the sea may have an effect on respiration, an experiment was made measuring respiration at different depths (Fig. 44). The effect was as might be expected greatest at the surface and decreased rapidly with depth. At 10 metres and sometimes even at 5 metres the respiration was the same as that in the dark. Males were

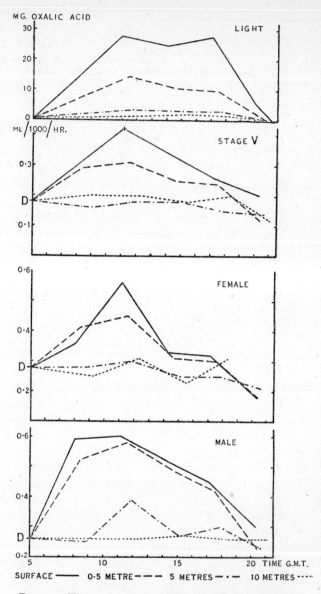

FIG. 44. The oxygen consumption at different depths in the sea and its relation to light intensity. D = value for oxygen consumption in the dark.

118

most affected and at noon showed a distinct rise in respiration at 5 metres; females were not so sensitive and Stage V least sensitive. These results were obtained with the first brood for the year which is found at the surface, and also with a summer brood. Klugh (1929, 1930) showed that the lethal effect of sunlight was caused chiefly by the ultra-violet component. Since ordinary glass cuts out much of the ultra-violet, respiration experiments were made at different depths using bottles of glass transparent to the ultra-violet. The respiration as before increased greatly at the surface but the part of the spectrum responsible was apparently still rapidly absorbed since the values at 10 metres were the same as those for the respiration in the dark. On the other hand there was a much higher mortality of *Calanus* in the bottles transparent to the ultra-violet than in ordinary glass bottles.

If copepods migrate downwards to avoid high light intensity because of its effect on respiration, one would expect this effect to extend beyond the top 5-10 metres. It would be interesting to know if the *Calanus* while swarming at the surface in bright light (p. 127) have a respiration much higher than normal.

Feeding is known to increase respiration in animals. The water was filtered before experiments with *Calanus* so as to reduce the likelihood of this having an appreciable effect on the results. The addition of food would complicate the measurement of respiration but it is likely that the effect of feeding on respiration would be obscured by other sources of variation.

The results on respiration recorded above were all made by measuring the oxygen consumption of a considerable number of animals in a relatively large volume of water. Later workers (Clarke and Bonnet, 1939; Raymont and Gauld, 1951) used smaller numbers of animals in small volumes of water. To measure respiration they used the Dixon-Haldane constant pressure apparatus (Dixon, 1943) with roughly two *Calanus* per ml of filtered sea water. The method has the advantage of giving more readings, being capable of greater accuracy and requiring fewer animals than the macro-method. On the other hand *Calanus* are in much less natural conditions owing to the greater crowding and more particularly the shaking of the vessel. Raymont and Gauld obtained significantly higher results when the respirometer was not shaken than when it was shaken, the reverse of what would have been expected if the disturbance had caused greater activity. The low results when shaking could not be attributed to the *Calanus* being damaged since they had a very low death rate (about 1%) and the majority of the animals were alive and active on the following day.

Clarke and Bonnet limited the shaking to five or ten minutes before taking a reading since they found continuous or rapid shaking resulted in a poor survival. The results obtained by Clarke and Bonnet and by Raymont and Gauld are similar to and only slightly higher than those obtained by Marshall, Nicholls and Orr (1935). The differences between all three sets of observations are probably not significant since the respiration shows considerable variations.

Raymont and Gauld also did some measurements in the light and in the dark with Stage V *Calanus* and concluded that light had no effect. Their experiments however were made in weak diffuse light, which is not strong enough to affect the respiration. As Fig. 44 shows Stage V is sensitive to strong light.

It would be most interesting to have measurements of respiration for the earlier copepodite stages of *Calanus* and for the nauplii. Raymont and Gauld give average figures for Stage IV *Calanus* of 0·25 μlO$_2$/copepod/hour at 17°C. For the earlier stages a more sensitive type of respirometer is required. Zeuthen (1947) gives measurements of the respiration of various copepods, mostly unidentified, using the Cartesian diver technique (Linderstrøm-Lang, 1937) which seems well suited for the work. We can obtain approximate figures for the respiration of the earlier copepodite stages of *Calanus* by extrapolation on the graph given by Raymont and Gauld relating copepodite length to respiration. When plotted on logarithmic co-ordinates the respiration of *Centropages*, *Calanus* and *Euchaeta* of different sizes was found to be on an approximate straight line whose equation is Log $R = 2\cdot19$ Log $L - 0\cdot928$. The smallest copepod used, *Centropages hamatus*, has a length of 0·86 mm and the largest, *Euchaeta norvegica*, 5·1 mm. Table XI shows the calculated values for the respiration of the copepodite stages of *Calanus* using the average length over the year for each stage given by Marshall, Nicholls and Orr (1934).

TABLE XI

Copepodite Stage	Respiration: μlO$_2$/copepod/hour			
	From curve $\log R = 2\cdot19$ $\log L - 0\cdot98$	Raymont and Gauld (17°C)	Clarke and Bonnet (15-17°C)	Marshall, Nicholls and Orr (15°C)
VI♀	0·89	0·87	—	0·61
VI♂	0·88	0·86	—	0·57
V	0·75	0·53	0·8-0·98	0·46
IV	0·40	0·25	—	—
III	0·22	—	—	—
II	0·11	—	—	—
I	0·05	—	—	—

The results obtained by calculation are apparently higher than those obtained experimentally and we may therefore expect that for the earlier copepodite stages also they are too high. The difference in the results obtained by Clarke and Bonnet, and by Marshall, Nicholls and Orr are not caused solely, and perhaps not at all, by the method of measurement, for Clarke and Bonnet obtained high results when control experiments were made using the Winkler method for estimating the oxygen. The high results of Raymont and Gauld on the other hand are more puzzling since they used *Calanus* from the same locality as Marshall, Nicholls and Orr.

Measurements of the respiration of *Calanus* are useful for estimating the food requirements since there is a quantitative relationship between the oxygen consumption and the material oxidized to produce energy. It is a pity that no figures for carbon dioxide production are available since this would allow us to estimate the respiratory quotient and therefore the kind of food used. Pütter (1924-25) calculated from the oxygen consumption that a *Calanus* requires as food 39% of its body weight per day and that a smaller copepod (*Oithona*) requires 60% of its body weight per day. This involves a very large intake of food and if this food consists of diatoms or other microplankton organisms, the number required is very much higher than is ever found in the sea.

For *Calanus* Pütter recorded a utilization of 1·83 μlO$_2$/copepod/hour (1922) or roughly two to three times the values found later by other workers. From January to March the Stage V *Calanus* in the Clyde area weighed about 0·15 mg per individual and the oxygen consumption at 5°C was about 0·17 μl/*Calanus*/hour. From April to July they weighed an average of about 0·30 mg and the oxygen consumption was about 0·42 μl/*Calanus*/hour at 15°C. From these figures it follows that the food requirements of Stage V *Calanus* in winter lie between 0·002 and 0·006 mg per individual per day and in summer between 0·005 and 0·013 mg. In each case the lower value given is that for fat and the higher that for carbohydrate. The true value will lie somewhere between these. These figures indicate that for Stage V the amount of food required daily, expressed as a percentage of the body weight (dry) of one *Calanus*, lies between 1·3% and 3·6% in winter and 1·7% and 4·5% in summer. In bright light the percentage lies between 2·2 and 2·8 in winter and 6·2 and 7·6 in summer. All these values are very much lower than that calculated by Pütter for *Calanus*.

Very little is known of the manner of uptake of oxygen by *Calanus*. According to Krogh (1941) copepods can obtain the necessary oxygen by diffusion through the surface and the exchange of gases probably takes place wherever the blood sinuses lie close to the cuticle, e.g. in the antennules and the lateral sinuses. Thus in *Calanus* the feeding currents described by Cannon (1928) may be partly respiratory. By means of the appendages round the mouth a current is passed from the posterior end forwards. When, in contrast to the normal so-called feeding movement, a *Calanus* makes one of its rapid escape movements the swimming feet are

I

moved vigorously and will furnish a good surface for oxygen exchange. The body fluid is kept in circulation by the rapidly beating heart and the movements of the appendages. The circulation has been described in Chapter II.

It has been suggested that there may also be anal respiration in *Calanus*. When an individual is watched under the microscope a reversed peristalsis is visible for a short distance at the anal end of the gut. Hartog (1888) was a strong supporter of the view that anal respiration is important in the crustacea. He noted that under normal conditions the rhythmic contractions are perfectly regular, that slight pressure reduces and greater pressure increases them. He contended that these contractions are not essential for defaecation and that indeed they are interrupted for some time when the lower part of the intestine is filled with faeces. Immediately after defaecation the activity is increased as though to make up for the temporary cessation of anal respiration. This reversed peristalsis or anal respiration certainly involves only very small quantities of water and it seems improbable that the transference of oxygen across the thinner wall of the gut is as important as what can be transferred from the large volumes of water passing the appendages.

Fox (1952) has recently discussed the function of oral and anal uptake of water by crustacea and comes to the conclusion that it is not respiratory. According to him the reversed anal peristalsis causes an uptake of water whose effect is to extend the walls of the main part of the gut, so increasing peristalsis there and facilitating defaecation.

CHAPTER IX

VERTICAL MIGRATION

IT has long been known that the vertical distribution of *Calanus*, as of many other plankton animals, varies considerably both throughout the day and from one season to another. For plankton in general our knowledge has been well summarized by Russell (1927), whose paper should be consulted for the earlier work on *Calanus*; a recent review by Cushing (1951) deals with planktonic crustacea.

SEASONAL VERTICAL MIGRATION

In general over-wintering *Calanus* remain in deep water in a pre-adult stage, and do not undertake diurnal vertical migrations. There is a gradual change in behaviour from the Arctic southwards. In the Barents Sea (Bogorov, 1934; Manteufel, 1941), in the fjords of East Greenland (Ussing, 1938) and near the Lofoten Islands (Sømme, 1934; Wiborg, 1954) *Calanus* spends the winter mainly in deep water as copepodite Stages II to V. During part of the winter in the Arctic there is no alternation of light and darkness and according to Bogorov *Calanus* shows no diurnal migration. A small number of *Calanus* however are always found in the surface waters there even during the winter. It should be noted that the term 'surface water' as used by the various authors is rather vague and may include depths down to 50 or even 100 m.

In January and February the population in the Arctic begins to ascend from deep water; the copepods begin to moult to adults and the females are fertilized. In due course they lay their eggs which develop and hatch in the surface waters. In the Barents Sea this generation while developing keeps close to the surface so that in the Arctic summer Stages III to V, which have a bright red colour and are present in immense concentrations give the sea a characteristic appearance. These copepodites descend to deep water again when the temperature rises in July and August. They show diurnal vertical migration in autumn and spend the winter in deep water once more.

Farther south along the coast of Norway also *Calanus* spends the winter in deep water and comes to the surface to spawn in March or April. Later in the year (in July) they descend to deep water. Ostvedt (1953) took samples from deep water in the Norwegian Sea (66°N; 2°E) and found that even the *Calanus* living below 1000 m took part in the spring migration to the surface. He supposes that light cannot be an effective stimulus at such depths and that migration must therefore be initiated by a change in the physiological condition caused by the developing gonad.

In the Clyde sea area *Calanus* in winter is found mainly below 100 m, and the over-wintering Stage V do not show diurnal vertical migration. After moulting has taken place in January and February the adults do not move upwards to live in the surface water as they do farther north but the females, in contrast to the males, show a marked diurnal vertical migration. They spawn in February to March and it is the generation resulting from this spawning which lives during April and May almost entirely at the surface and spawns there in May. A possible relation between vertical migration and egg laying has been discussed on p. 41. The period during which the *Calanus* move down again usually coincides with the transition between the first and second generations (Fig. 45). The extent of the migration to the surface varies however and in exceptional years, such as 1926 and 1932, *Calanus* were not taken at the surface in large numbers even in April and May. Little is known about the factors causing them to leave the surface. In the Clyde area the descent of adult and Stage V *Calanus* occurs about a month before that of the small species of copepod (Marshall, 1949) in which it does not seem to be correlated with generations.

In the English Channel (Russell, 1934*a*) it seems to be a later generation still which comes to the surface and it does so in July or August (Fig. 46). The form there, however, is *C. helgolandicus*.

There is no simple explanation of these movements to and from the surface. In contrast to Ostvedt, Ussing believes the spawning migration to be initiated by the increasing light. If this is so *Calanus* must be extremely sensitive to light for the change in intensity below 1000 m or even below 100 m in February to March in the Arctic must be very small. Increasing temperature has been suggested as one cause of the retreat to deep water later in the year and if it is, the critical temperature obviously must vary with the region in which the *Calanus* are caught. It has also been suggested that they stay constantly in the deep cold water during the winter to conserve their energy when food is scarce (see also p. 159). The cessation of diurnal migration will certainly conserve energy but during the winter it is often precisely this deep water which is the warmest.

The congregation of enormous numbers of *Calanus* right at the surface

FIG. 45.   Seasonal migration in *Calanus*. Percentage of stages above and below 10 m in Loch Striven, 1933.

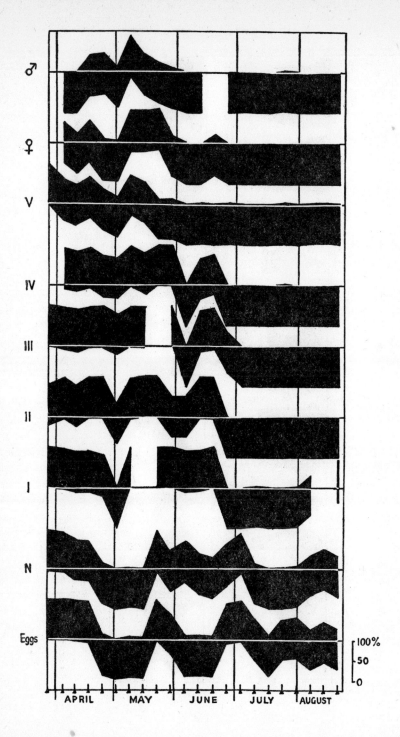

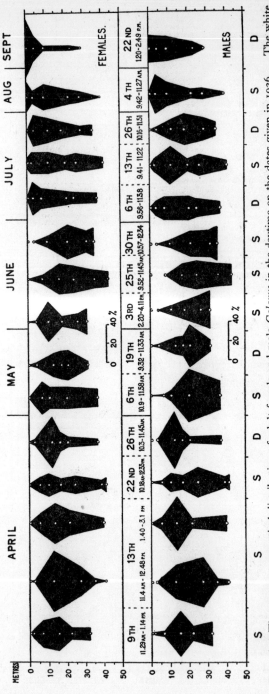

Fig. 46. The percentage vertical distribution of adult female and male *Calanus* in the daytime on the dates given in 1926. The white spots and black circles indicate the average depths at which the hauls were made. The times given are G.M.T. and show the duration of the series of hauls. S, sunny; D, dull.

during the summer is a very striking phenomenon especially since it is opposed to their usual behaviour. It is a common sight in the Clyde on calm days during May and June to see the surface of the sea covered with small circles of expanding ripples like those caused by raindrops. These are usually caused by copepods, often *Calanus*, bumping against the surface film. This behaviour is not limited to dull days but may occur even in bright sunshine. It has been observed by many workers in many different places (Roussel de Vauzème, 1834; Goodsir, 1843; Brook, 1886; Herdman, 1919; Willey, 1919; Bigelow, 1926; Marshall and Orr, 1927; Ruud, 1929; Nicholls, 1933*b*; Gardiner, 1933).

In 1843 Goodsir thus described them: 'On looking into the water it was found to be quite obscured by the moving masses of Entomostraca which rendered it impossible to see anything even a few inches below the surface. But if a clear spot is obtained so as to allow the observer to get a view of the bottom, immense shoals of coalfish are seen swimming lazily about, and devouring their minute prey in great quantities.' On a visit to the Isle of May in the Firth of Forth he noticed that at some distance from land the sea had taken on a red colour and that 'the surface of the water presented a very curious appearance, as if a quantity of fine sand were constantly falling on it. I thought at first that this last circumstance proceeded from rain, but presently I found that both phenomena were caused by a great number of small red Entomostraca.' They were later identified as *Calanus*. The appearance is caused by the *Calanus* actually bumping against the surface film. Ruud says that to Norwegian fishermen and whalers in the waters off Möre it is a common phenomenon. He himself has observed *Calanus* 'right at the surface, like red clouds' only on three occasions, once in March and twice in July. Each time they were being eaten by whales and basking sharks.

Detailed observations on the behaviour of these surface *Calanus* have been made in the Clyde area by Bainbridge (1952) who used a frogman's suit. He could see the copepods clearly even four or five feet away. There were two zones of differing behaviour clearly recognizable. In the foot of water just under the surface there was a high concentration of *Calanus* and a continuous gentle sinking and swimming up again vertically within this zone. Their distribution was extremely patchy and they were often aggregated just under the surface into little groups of a dozen or so which swam round and round each other. Most of the movement was vertical although occasionally, especially when two animals came close to one another, there might be violent oblique or horizontal leaps of several feet. A good deal of horizontal movement also resulted from a kind of bouncing against the underside of the surface film. Below the upper zone was another of indeterminate depth in which *Calanus* were scarcer and more evenly distributed. Here there were about equal numbers swimming vertically upwards and vertically downwards. Two or three individuals were followed; they left the surface zone and swam steadily downwards for five or six feet where they turned upright and hung motionless for a short time before swimming steadily up into the surface zone again. Others swam to and from layers deeper than this and Bainbridge suggests that there may be a continual interchange between the population at the surface and that in deep water. A large proportion, usually half, and in dull weather sometimes almost all, were hanging quite motionless in the water. This observation confirms those of Lowndes (1935) that *Calanus* can apparently remain at one level without swimming upwards. While making observations in a plankton wheel (see p. 139) Hardy and Bainbridge (1954) found that the regular movements of *Calanus* were rarely lateral but almost always vertically upwards or downwards. The position of rest is always with the head upwards and it often sinks slowly in this position, but it can also turn round and swim down.

DIURNAL VERTICAL MIGRATION

The knowledge that many plankton animals undertake every day extensive migrations from deep water to the surface and back has interested biologists for many years and much work has been done to find the reason. *Calanus* being a readily available and abundant copepod has been the most closely studied of the marine crustacea for this purpose. It must be emphasized however that our knowledge of vertical migration is based on comparatively few series of observations and considering how much it varies between different stages and at different times of the year further work is much needed.

In the Arctic (Bogorov, 1946) the changes in diurnal vertical migration throughout the year are marked. During the continuous darkness of the Arctic winter there is none although the *Calanus* are not passive. They keep at their chosen depth in spite of tidal and other movements tending to cause a change in level. In spring, when a day and night rhythm in light has begun, they come to the surface for spawning and the next generation remains there during the continuous light of the summer. A limited amount of vertical migration may go on even when the population is living near the surface. In Tromsø Sound in March 1952 when the *Calanus* had come up from deep water to spawn, we found that they were more abundant at 20 to 40 m during the day and at 0 to 10 m during the night. Similar observations have recently been made by Wiborg, 1954. In late summer the Arctic *Calanus* descend to deep water and with the return to a day and night light rhythm in autumn, a marked diurnal migration begins.

In temperate regions conditions seem to be more complicated. The most detailed work has been done by Russell (1925, 1926, 1928a and b), Nicholls (1933b), Clarke (1933, 1934a and c) and Farran (1947).

Russell was the first to carry out detailed observations at different depths in the sea with special attention to light conditions. On a moonlit night in July 1924, he found that *Calanus* (males, females and Stage V but mostly females) rose to the surface at dusk, scattered throughout the water during the dark hours and collected again before dawn at about 10 m to move downwards. On two successive moonless nights in the following June rather similar results were obtained but the *Calanus* did not mass at the surface at dusk or at 10 m at dawn, nor was the distribution during the darkest hours so even. He suggested that the *Calanus* kept within an optimum light intensity and that this moved towards the surface as dusk fell and down again after dawn. During the dark hours all stimulus disappeared and the *Calanus* moved randomly and became evenly distributed from top to bottom. He thought that the differences between the two sets of observations might be due to the differing light intensities on the two dates. In later observations (Russell, 1934a) he found that both males and females had very different optimum light intensities in July from those in August.

Clarke, working in the Gulf of Maine, correlated his results with light measurements taken in the sea at the same time. In his first observations in 1933 the results with *Calanus* were rather irregular and only females showed a definite migration. Later on (Clarke, 1934a) diurnal migration was studied on five successive days in July, on the first three at a station in the deepest part of the Gulf of Maine (170 m), on the last two about 100 miles south on the eastern edge of a submarine bank (70 m). Copepodites from Stage III to adult were investigated although Stage III were rare at the deep station. The most striking fact is the completely different picture given by the migrations at these two stations, where the environmental conditions were not very different. At the deep station all *Calanus* from Stage IV to adult showed a rapid migration upwards as darkness fell and a rapid migration downwards starting at sunrise (Fig. 47). The rise to the surface was later on 14th July than 15th or 16th July, and, on the whole, when rising, the copepods kept at an intensity (measured photoelectrically) of between 0·1 and 1·0 μ W. There was an extraordinary similarity between the distributions of all the stages; they lived at the same depths and migrated to the same extent, which is quite contrary to experience elsewhere.

At the shallow station, worked on 17th-18th July the copepods were concentrated in the top 30 to 40 m, there was very little migration at all and they were subjected to a range of light intensities from 0 to more than

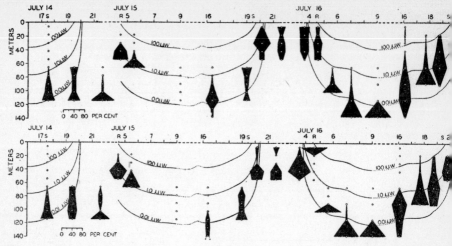

FIG. 47. Diurnal migration during a 54-hour period at the deep station. For explanation
Fig. 48.

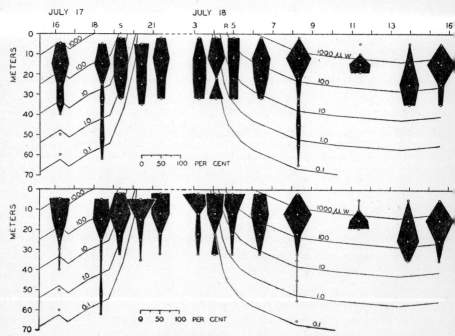

FIG. 48. Diurnal migration during a 24-hour period at the shallow station.
The black circles and white dots indicate the depth at which the hauls were made. The chan
in the intensity of the blue component of daylight are shown by the lines representing the depth
which 100 microwatts/cm², 1 microwatt/cm² etc. occurred. Broken lines indicate a shorter
of the time scale; observations were not discontinued during these periods. S, sunset; R, suns
upper figure, males; lower, females.

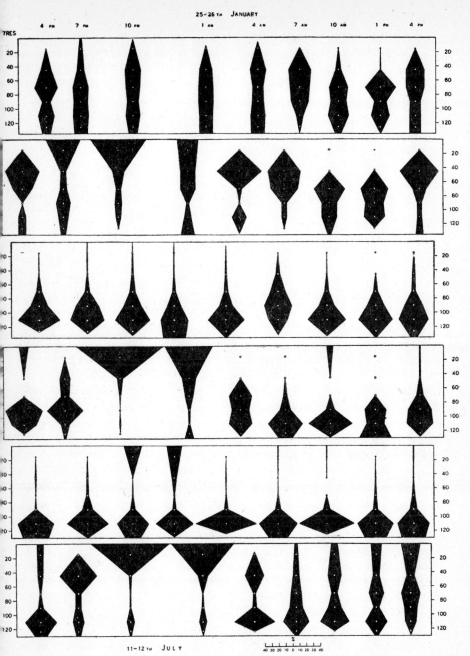

9. Diagram showing vertical distribution at 3-hourly intervals during 24-hour periods on Jan. 25th-and July 11th-12th in Loch Fyne, 1932. Sunset Jan. 25th at 4.27 p.m., sunrise Jan. 26th at 8.37 sunset July 11th at 8.27 p.m., sunrise July 12th at 3.58 a.m. (*a*) Males, January; (*b*) Females, ary; (*c*) Stage V, January; (*d*) Females, July; (*e*) Stage V, July; (*f*) Stage IV, July.

1000 μ W (Fig. 48). Again the behaviour of all stages from III to adult resembled one another closely. At this same station, however, another copepod *Metridia lucens* showed a typical diurnal migration from 60–70 m up to the surface and back.

Measurements were made of copepods from samples from the two stations but the lengths did not differ appreciably. Clarke suggests that the most likely explanation of the difference in behaviour is a physiological differentiation caused by different environments.

Clarke confirmed what had already been suggested by Russell, that light adaptation takes place and that the optimum intensity rises somewhat by day, dropping again after the dark hours. He also found that a greater change was necessary to initiate migration than to maintain it.

Nicholls (1933*b*) carried out similar observations in the Clyde area with the object of finding out whether the migration varied with the season. He realized later that although his observations were made in January and July yet, since little breeding goes on after July the *Calanus* on both occasions belonged to the over-wintering generation. In January only Stage V and adults were present, in July all copepodite stages but the male.

In January the males (Fig. 49*a*) showed a slight but definite extension of their distribution into the upper layers during the dark hours. The females (Fig. 49*b*), whose depth of maximum abundance was always above that of the males, showed a very clear migration upwards at dusk, an even distribution at 1 a.m., a concentration at about 40 m at 4 a.m. and a subsequent movement downwards. Stage V (Fig. 49*c*) showed practically no migration, remaining most abundant both day and night in the deep water below 80 m.

In July Stages I to III stayed continuously above 40 m. Stages IV (Fig. 49*f*) showed a clear migration upwards at dusk and were concentrated in the upper layers at 10 p.m. and 1 a.m.—after which they moved down. During the day, however, there was a slight movement upwards again and a rather even distribution from top to bottom. The bulk of the Stage V (Fig. 49*e*) remained in deep water below 100 m which was deeper than they were found in winter. In contrast to the winter, however, a proportion of them were found in the surface waters at 10 p.m. and 1 a.m. Females migrated (Fig. 49*d*) as before but, compared with the winter they were, like Stage V, deeper during the day, and at 10 p.m. and 1 a.m. they were more concentrated at the surface.

Farran's (1947) observations off the south of Ireland in 1931–32 resemble Nicholls' results, although the male *Calanus* showed more migration and the Stage IV less.

As already mentioned nauplii and eggs are found mainly near the surface.

From all these observations we can see that there is a great variation in behaviour, not only between different places, different seasons and different developmental stages, but even from day to day. It should be noted too that even in the same population some animals always behave differently from the rest. For example in Nicholls' experiments, when the Stage V in July were keeping mainly below 100 m, there were always a few, and at 10 p.m. and 1 a.m. a considerable number, to be found above. Nicholls suggested that the actual state of development within the stage might have an effect. Thus the Stage V which had just moulted from Stage IV might continue their diurnal migrations for a day or two and the Stage V approaching the moult to female might begin migrating again. In the same way Stage IV is intermediate between a surface and a deep-living stage, both non-migratory, and its behaviour might be modified accordingly. In females one might expect that they would be influenced by the state of the ovary. Both Russell and Clarke have suggested that the reactions of a *Calanus* may be altered by a physiological change in response to its environment and this opens up a wide field for speculation and research.

Although the seasonal migrations may be caused by temperature changes there is little evidence that their diurnal movements are affected by normal temperature or salinity gradients, even where there is a marked discontinuity layer. Clarke (1934a) showed that they can climb through a thermocline of 6°C over Georges Bank. Esterly (1912) had earlier shown that off the coast of California they climbed from a temperature of 9°C in deep water during the day to 17°C near the surface at night. Nikitine (1929) on the other hand found that *Calanus* in the Black Sea was stopped by the 13° isotherm and Farran (1947) found that the early copepodites remained below the thermocline.

Some interesting observations were made by Hansen (1951) in June in the Oslo fjord. The position of the discontinuity layer was found by means of the bathythermograph and hauls taken above, below, and in it. Female *Calanus* did not go below the discontinuity layer and kept within it except when they migrated into the surface layers at about midnight; males did not migrate but kept more strictly in or close to the discontinuity layer; Stage V seemed to be uninfluenced by it and were more evenly distributed. A comparison with results from other times of the year would be interesting.

Esterly (1912) concluded that the diurnal temperature variation, which is extremely small, did not cause or even affect the diurnal vertical migration since at any depth this variation is only a small fraction of the range the animal passes through. Clarke came to the same conclusion.

Since their food lives mainly at the surface they must come up to feed and they perhaps avoid the surface during the daylight hours because they are then more visible to predators. Hardy (Hardy and Gunther, 1935) suggested that when phytoplankton is present in strong concentrations it is injurious to zooplankton and is avoided by it. The richer the concentration the shorter will be the time spent in it. Since currents in deep water often move at a different speed or in a different direction from those at the surface the zooplankton in such areas, by spending a longer or a shorter time in the deep current, can be carried away from the phytoplankton-rich areas.

Some phytoplankton organisms are undoubtedly avoided by animals and a clear instance of this is given by the avoidance of rich concentrations of *Phaeocystis* ('baccy-juice') by shoals of herring (Savage, 1930). Some other members of the phytoplankton are known to be injurious to a variety of animals though little or nothing has been done on their effect on the zooplankton.

It has been suggested (Nathansohn, 1909; Akehurst, 1931; Lucas, 1938) that a diatom culture may excrete some substance injurious to its own growth. It is possible that during phytoplankton increases in the sea substances are excreted which are harmful also to zooplankton.

It has often been observed that zooplankton and phytoplankton are not present in large quantities in the same area. Such a distribution has been described in the English Channel (Harvey, 1934) and in the North Sea (Wimpenny, 1937) as well as in the Antarctic (Hardy and Gunther, 1935). In the Arctic also Manteufel (1941) observed that the 'red' *Calanus* which congregate in great quantities at the surface do not occur in the richest patches of the diatoms but some distance from them. There are different explanations possible for this; the zooplankton may be avoiding the phytoplankton according to the exclusion hypothesis, or the zooplankton may have eaten the phytoplankton which was originally there as Harvey suggested (see also Chapter XI).

Bainbridge (1949) using, it is true, only estuarine plankton found a migration towards, and not away from, water rich in diatoms. He also found (1953) that in vertical tubes more *Calanus* swam upwards in the presence of cultures of diatoms and some flagellates than in filtered sea water. This shows clearly that an external factor other than light can have some effect on vertical movement.

It is now generally agreed that the immediate stimulus to diurnal migration is light, perhaps modified in extreme cases by temperature (see above). The conception of an optimum light intensity inside which the copepods keep, each stage and each population having perhaps its own optimum, has proved the most fruitful explanation of their movements. Clarke (1934c) and Cushing (1951) have suggested that their movements are random and that they move more quickly in the light than in the dark but this is contradicted by Bainbridge's observations in the sea (p. 127). We have little knowledge of the value of these migrations to the animal. The fact that they are so regular and so extensive indicates that they must play some important part in the life history.

More recently Hardy (1953) has suggested that vertical migration is a means evolved to enable the animals to sample fresh bodies of water. No innate physiological rhythm of migration has been observed and if it were possible for *Calanus* to stop migrating when they enter a body of water with optimal conditions this might explain the great differences of behaviour at different times. Harris (1953) however suggests that vertical migration habits were acquired as an accidental consequence of using light as a means of depth control.

EXPERIMENTAL WORK

It is not surprising that many workers have tried to analyse the diurnal movements of *Calanus* in the laboratory where each external factor can be controlled and its effect studied separately. Even then, however, the problem is not simple.

Esterly (1919) and Rose (1925) are among the earlier authors who made experiments both in the sea and in the laboratory. Rose made experiments on the effect of temperature and thought that it was dominant at over 20°C. Esterly however found that *Calanus* was 'negative' to light of all intensities except when the water was cold. He says that the phototropism becomes noticeably positive at about 13°C and is pronouncedly so at temperatures below 10°C. It is obvious that in the sea there are many exceptions to these experimental findings.

Esterly also found that copepods caught near the surface had reactions to light different from those of copepods caught in deep water; laboratory conditions too might affect their behaviour. Rose, by using tubes which could be partially darkened found that in general copepods did not necessarily avoid or seek light; if placed in light below a lower limit of intensity they moved towards the light, and if in light above an upper limit of intensity they moved away from it; between these two intensities they were indifferent and moved randomly. This led to the 'optimum intensity' hypothesis. Rose concluded that normally light has a predominant effect on migration but that temperature can also be important and that other factors can have an influence too.

Friedrich (1931) showed that *Calanus helgolandicus* always travelled towards the source of light but that it was affected to a greater or lesser extent by lateral illumination and usually turned towards this even if its intensity were somewhat less than the first source. The structure of the eye may help to explain this (see p. 23). Spooner (1933) made some interesting observations on copepods, although not on *Calanus*, and thought that they moved towards the light source irrespective of accompanying changes in intensity in the surroundings. The bearing of the experiments of Friedrich and of Spooner on vertical migration is not clear; the light used was presumably below the optimum intensity for the copepods. Recent experiments by Harris (1953) have shown how changes in light may affect the swimming movements and therefore the migrations of *Daphnia*.

Experiments by Huntsman (1924), Harvey (1930), Klugh (1930) and Marshall, Nicholls and Orr (1935) all show that bright light may be harmful to *Calanus*. Huntsman showed that *Calanus* is unable to withstand the action of ordinary sunlight even after it has passed through a considerable thickness of glass. Klugh extended these observations and showed that, with filters allowing the ultra-violet component to pass, sunlight killed *Calanus* in an average of 36 hours. These observations on the lethal effect of sunlight have often been confirmed at Millport where it has been found to kill in much less than 36 hours. Not only sunlight, but bright diffuse daylight is lethal. The effect is not caused by temperature since it is found even at temperatures close to 0°C. *Calanus* from the brood which lives at the surface, however, seem to be much less affected by sunlight. Females and Stage V were taken in May from the surface metre and were exposed both in the sea and in the open air at constant temperature in sunny weather. Most survived more than two days' exposure although they became sluggish.

Harvey measured the rate of heart-beat of *Calanus* at different temperatures and under different light conditions. When exposed to direct sunlight at 13°C the heart-beat rate decreased steadily over four days from about 300 to about 130 beats per minute. A short exposure to sunlight was not always fatal; *Calanus* sometimes recovered after four hours exposure but not after 8 hours. Harvey found the blue end of the spectrum more injurious than the red or green or even than the whole spectrum, providing the energy values remained the same.

Marshall, Nicholls and Orr when investigating the respiration of *Calanus* exposed them to daylight in clear glass bottles at controlled temperatures. They found that in bright diffuse light or in sunshine the respiration of all stages might be double what it was in the dark. Although the results are physiologically extremely interesting it is difficult to see how they could affect vertical migration. In the first place the lethal ultra-violet light is rapidly absorbed and would not affect the *Calanus* in deep water. According to Atkins and Poole (1933) the intensity is reduced to 1% at 2·1 m (wave length 303 mμ). The effect of light on respiration also decreases rapidly with depth (Fig. 44). At the surface it was considerable, at 0·5 m it was still noticeable but at 5 m and 10 m there was hardly any effect. When returned to the dark after exposure to light the respiration was depressed for some considerable time, which suggests that the *Calanus* had been injured. In view of all these facts it is very difficult to understand why some broods of *Calanus* should be found actually bouncing against the surface film in bright sunlight.

There is no doubt but that much of the experimental work done in the laboratory on *Calanus* is affected by changes in the animals themselves. During the process of capture and sorting they have already been exposed to conditions very different from their natural environment and their behaviour may be quite abnormal. The higher respiration found by Marshall, Nicholls and Orr (see p. 115) during the first 24 hours after capture may have been an effect of this disturbance. It occurred even if precautions were taken to keep *Calanus* in the dark throughout.

In order to avoid disturbing the animals, and also to have conditions as natural as possible, Hardy and Paton (1947) carried out experiments on the migration of *Calanus* in the sea itself. The experimental animals were enclosed in twin glass cylinders 1 m long with upper and lower compartments which could be either connected with, or separated from, one another by trap doors operated by messenger weights sent down the wire on which the apparatus was suspended. The *Calanus* were kept in the dark while they were being introduced into the cylinders and were never subjected to above-surface illumination. They were put into either the top or bottom half of the cylinders and when the apparatus had been lowered to the selected depth the compartments were put into communication with one another and left for a certain time (usually 1 hour). They were then separated again, the apparatus hauled up and the *Calanus* from the four compartments counted separately.

Experiments done at different depths (Fig. 50) showed that the deeper the cylinders were exposed the smaller was the percentage of *Calanus* moving downwards and this effect was not due to the depth at which they had been caught nor, so far as the authors could judge, was it correlated with the changing light intensity at the different depths. That the response was, however, caused by light and not by gravity was shown in experiments where one of the cylinders was darkened and lit by reflection from mirrors underneath.

Their experiments did not confirm the suggestion that in complete darkness *Calanus* moved randomly; instead a large proportion was found moving actively downwards and a small proportion upwards. Indeed the behaviour in darkened and undarkened cylinders was very similar.

Thus two very puzzling facts emerged from these interesting experi-

K

ments. The first was that at whatever depth the *Calanus* were caught, in the cylinders some were always moving actively upwards and some downwards. The second was that behaviour in complete darkness was very

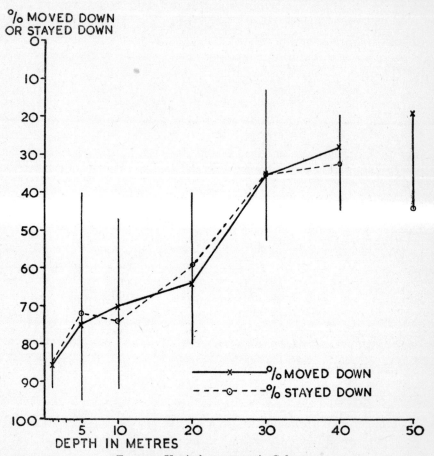

FIG. 50.   Vertical movement in *Calanus*.

The crosses, connected by a continuous line, represent the average percentage values of Stage V which moved down in all standard experiments, and the points within circles, connected by a broken line, represent the average percentage which have stayed down. The divergent results at 50 m depth are based on only one experiment of each kind. The vertical lines show the range.

(After Hardy and Paton.)

similar to that in the light. These facts seem contradictory and Hardy's tentative suggestion that *Calanus* might have a 'sense of depth', the stimulus to migration being normally given by changing light intensity, is not supported by his later experiments with Bainbridge (Hardy and

Bainbridge, 1951) on the effect of pressure. These showed that change in pressure, at least up to that equivalent to a depth of 20 m, had no effect on the vertical distribution in cylinders in the laboratory.

The methods used by Hardy and Paton were extremely ingenious and when the work was stopped in 1939, development was in the direction of using longer and longer cylinders. The logical result has been the construction of a tube in the form of a large wheel giving in effect an infinitely long tube. The wheel is moved on its axle to keep the experimental animals in a known position and the movements recorded on a smoked drum. It was found (Hardy and Bainbridge, 1954) that over a short period (2 minutes) *Calanus* could swim upwards at a speed of 66 metres per hour and downwards at 107 m/hr. Over a longer period (1 hour), however, comparable speeds were 15 m/hr upwards and 47 m/hr downwards.

In their movements there was a great deal of individual variation even when using the same animal under similar conditions, but on the whole the tendency was to move upwards in the evening as the light decreased and downwards during the day. With the spring surface living generation at Millport however the effect might be completely reversed and the *Calanus* swim upwards even in bright sunshine. Artificial blacking out during the day only sometimes caused an upward movement. It is clear from the experiments that light, although important, is not the only factor influencing diurnal vertical migration.

Zeuthen (1947) has pointed out that animals which normally sink in the water must expend energy to keep at a constant level. The rate of sinking of dead and of anaesthetized *Calanus* in sea water has been measured by Gardiner (1933) and by Gross and Raymont (1942) and in addition Lowndes (1942) has measured its density. This he expresses as its 'sinking factor' which is the ratio of the density of the organism to the density of the sea water multiplied by 1000. For *Calanus* he obtained in two experiments at 15·4°C values of 1029 and 1033. One would expect the sinking factor to change seasonally since the fat content changes so markedly (Marshall, Nicholls and Orr, 1934); there will probably also be differences in male, female and the earlier copepodite stages. A *Calanus* may lose a little of its oil from the oil sac without any apparent ill effect although this loss must increase its density.

From the rates of sinking measured by Gardiner and by Gross and Raymont one might expect sinking to be an important factor in the vertical migration of *Calanus* in the sea and indeed it has generally been assumed that the downward movement of *Calanus* in the sea is a passive sinking. The detailed observations of Lowndes (1935) in the laboratory and those of Bainbridge (1952) in the sea suggest however that the actual rate of sinking in the sea when the *Calanus* is passive is much lower than would be expected from the experiments on dead or narcotized *Calanus*; it may indeed be negligible.

Lowndes noted that the behaviour differed in still and in disturbed water. In still water in the laboratory *Calanus* is 'at times, and for long periods, remarkably non-motile'. Unlike other species it is in his opinion 'a true floating organism. The animal remains in a vertical position, with the antennules stretched out to their fullest extent, and does not sink appreciably during quite long intervals'. In disturbed water, e.g. in a plunger jar, he found a different type of movement. As before 'the antennules are held straight out and the animal is generally in a vertical position, but it is continuously rising or falling. The rising is carried out quite clearly by the rapid vibration of the antennae, the mandibular palps, the maxillules and possibly the maxillipedes, but the action of the latter is irregular.' He observed also that the sinking is not just the effect of gravity but that it is 'due to a definite swimming action and results chiefly from the antennae swinging through an angle of about 90°, so that the vibrations of the endopodite constitute a backward component'.

Bainbridge's observations in the sea have not confirmed this second movement although he agrees that *Calanus* can apparently remain at one level without swimming upwards. He observed too that *Calanus* going downwards were not sinking passively, nor going slowly downwards as observed by Lowndes in the laboratory but were inverted and swimming actively downwards. It is improbable that any other mode of locomotion would be rapid enough to account for the known considerable downward migration.

Little is known of the energy expenditure required for a *Calanus* to carry out its migrations. Gray (1928) has shown that the work W done by a swimming micro-organism moving horizontally is $W = kV^2$ and that when moving vertically it is $W = M(\sigma - P)V + kV^2$ when V is the velocity k is a constant depending on the viscosity of the water, M is the mass of the organism and $(\sigma - P)$ is the difference between the specific gravity of the organism and the water. kV^2 is the work done in overcoming the viscous resistance of the water and $M(\sigma - P)V$ is the work done in raising the organism. Sufficient data are not yet available to enable us to calculate the work done by *Calanus* during its migrations but all the results seem to point to the conclusion that the chief work done by *Calanus* in moving in the sea is that of overcoming the viscous resistance of the water.

In spite of the large amount of observational and experimental work on *Calanus* we are still far from understanding fully why this small animal should expend so much energy daily in swimming up and down in the sea. It is obvious that no one explanation will cover all the different types of migration observed. The reaction to light of the *Calanus* which are seen bouncing against the surface film on a sunny day in June must be quite different from the reactions of those which leave the surface soon after midnight to spend the day in water below 100 m. Although light is probably of primary importance in initiating and perhaps controlling their movements, other factors must sometimes override it. Experiments and observations both in the sea and in the laboratory of the kind begun by Hardy, Paton and Bainbridge seem at present the most hopeful line of exploration.

CHAPTER X

PARASITES

THE parasites of *Calanus* are both varied and interesting although not all of them have been studied in detail. Some of them are external, some internal, either in the gut or in the body cavity. Some are found all the year round, others are more or less restricted to summer or winter. Many of the parasites found in *Calanus* are found also in other copepods and occasionally in other animals.

The incidence of parasitism as a whole is rather low but in the Clyde sea area it is highest in the over-wintering generation. This of course lives longest and is therefore longest exposed to infection, and occasionally the percentage parasitized is so high that the mortality from this cause alone may be considerable. For instance at Millport on 26th March 1931, of 363 female *Calanus* examined, over a fifth were parasitized, 42 with *Syndinium* or *Paradinium*, 27 with tetraphyllid and 3 with cyclophyllid cestode larvae, 6 with nematodes and 1 with *Ellobiopsis*. In the North Sea infection with *Blastodinium* alone may be 66%.

An occasional copepodite Stage III or IV is found parasitized but as a rule infection is confined to Stage V and adults and is heaviest in the females, next heaviest in Stage V. Jepps (1937*a*) has suggested that the lower incidence in the male may be because the parasite has prevented the development of male characters (as *Sacculina* does in crabs). There is, however, no good evidence to support this. Males, being shorter lived, are less suitable hosts than females or Stage V (see p. 79).

Parasitized specimens are as a rule less healthy and live a shorter time in the laboratory but when first captured they seem as active and agile as a normal *Calanus*. It is indeed astonishing to see how completely a *Calanus* may be filled with a plasmodial mass which has destroyed the gonad and is attacking the muscles, and yet retain its activity.

The effect produced by parasites is variable but it is a curious fact that several induce in their hosts a bright red colour. The colour is sometimes in the parasite itself (e.g. *Paradinium*) but is often an unusual development of the red pigment always found in *Calanus*. In normal specimens there is usually some of this pigment round the mouth as well as at the hind end of the metasome, associated with the gut or with the oil sac. Pigment is frequently found also along the antennules and occasionally in other

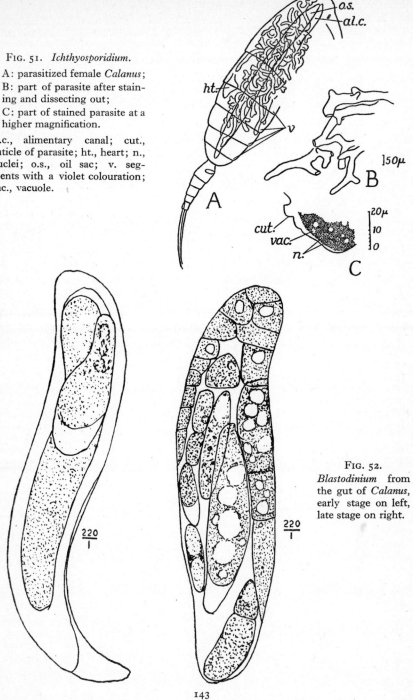

FIG. 51. *Ichthyosporidium.*

A: parasitized female *Calanus*;
B: part of parasite after staining and dissecting out;
C: part of stained parasite at a
higher magnification.

al.c., alimentary canal; cut.,
cuticle of parasite; ht., heart; n.,
nuclei; o.s., oil sac; v. segments with a violet colouration;
vac., vacuole.

o.s.
al.c.

ht.

v

]50μ

B

cut.
vac.
n.

20μ
10
0

C

A

FIG. 52.
Blastodinium from
the gut of *Calanus*,
early stage on left,
late stage on right.

$\frac{220}{1}$

$\frac{220}{1}$

143

limbs. Sometimes the oil itself has a faint pink tinge. The development of pigment varies greatly with the individual and is greater at some times of the year than at others. In *Calanus* parasitized with cestodes or trematodes, however, the whole animal is bright scarlet, while with protozoan infections of the body cavity the colour is rather orange or coral red. Nematodes also infect the body cavity but have little or no effect on the colour (see, however, p. 31); gut parasites and external parasites have none either. In any case the colour change of the host is a late development in the history of the infection; those *Calanus* with early parasitic stages look normal and, as Jepps (1937*a*) remarks, are usually found when examining sections of supposedly healthy animals.

Although on a close examination some parasites seem to have no injurious effect, most of them prevent the normal development of the gonad even when they do not (as does *Syndinium*) attack it directly. The large amount of material which should have gone towards egg production has probably been turned instead to the nutrition of the parasite.

In 1911 Apstein published a preliminary list of parasites in *Calanus* from the North Sea and Kattegat. He had to leave the work incomplete and gave only a numeral, a short description and usually a figure for each form. Chatton (1920) in his large work on the parasitic peridinians describes several of these forms and later Jepps (1937*a*) gave an account of all the protozoan parasites on *Calanus* from the Clyde sea area. She also (1937*b*) revised Apstein's list, identifying as many as possible of the organisms, and described the early stages of some cestode larvae. There follows here a list and short description of the parasites which have been recognized in *Calanus*.

Fungi

Ichthyosporidium (Fig. 51). This fungus was described by Apstein as occurring in *Calanus* from both the North Sea and Kattegat. It was found only once by Jepps in the Clyde samples. It forms a yellowish red mycelium branching through the metasome of the host. The cytoplasm is closely granular and contains numerous vesicular nuclei. Chatton has described it in the Mediterranean from other copepods, and it occurs also in salmonid fish. Apstein remarks that the *Calanus* were unaffected by the parasite and swam about actively; in the single specimen seen by Jepps the ovary was small but the eggs were not visibly degenerate.

Dinoflagellata

Blastodinium (Fig. 52). This was one of the commonest parasites in Apstein's samples and is considered by Chatton to be *B. hyalinum*, a northern form of *B. contortum*. Seymour Sewell (1951), however, con-

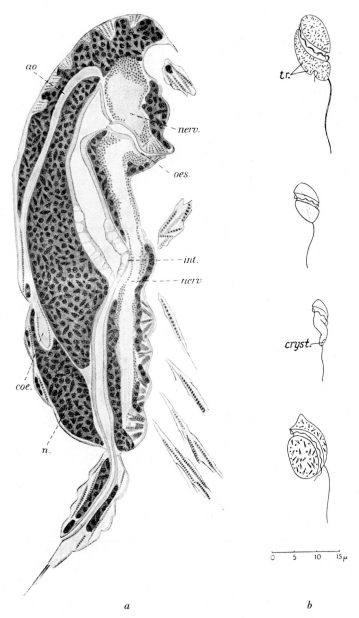

tr.

cryst.

0   5   10   15μ

a   *b*

FIG. 53.

(*a*) section of a *Paracalanus parvus* infected with *Syndinium*: ao, aorta; nerv.,
    brain and ventral nerve cord; oes., oesophagus; int., gut; coe., heart; n, nuclei
    in plasmodium.

(*b*) dinoflagellate spores from different copepods (after Chatton): cryst.,
    crystalline bodies; tr., trichites.

siders *B. hyalinum* to be a separate species. It was found only twice in Jepp's samples but since it, unlike other parasites, does not colour the *Calanus* it may easily be overlooked. It is a gut parasite and is enclosed in a thin smooth envelope. Chatton has found it common in copepodite stages from at least Stage III onwards. In contrast to other *Blastodinium* species it usually occurs singly in the host.

The long and slightly twisted cell divides obliquely to give an anterior trophocyte and a posterior gonocyte. The gonocyte continues to divide until it has formed a layer of sporocytes covering most of the trophocyte. In most species the envelope breaks at this stage, the sporocytes are released and the trophocyte reforms the envelope and divides to begin the process all over again. In *B. hyalinum* the trophocyte divides at a much earlier stage and thus a series of layers of sporocytes is found one inside the other.

After the sporocytes have been released they emerge by the anus and divide into two dinospores. These encyst and their later history has not been followed.

Vane (1952), who has studied *Blastodinium* in *Calanus* from plankton recorder hauls from the North Sea found that although infection on the average was low (3·7% in the total catch of females and Stage V) it might in some catches be as high as 66%. The peak of infection was in July and August. Chatton states that the infection prevents the normal development of the gonad. Cattley (1948) suggests that in *Pseudocalanus* the same species may in addition cause partial or complete sex reversal in the male, but Sewell (1951) argues convincingly against this hypothesis.

Syndinium (Fig. 53). The earliest known stage of this dinoflagellate is a small plasmodial mass, which is embedded in the connective tissue usually on the dorsal side of the mid-gut. At this stage it is encysted but as it grows the capsule wall disappears and the plasmodium develops into a lobed mass which gradually spreads through the body cavity flattening out against the body wall and creeping over the surface of the organs (Fig. 53*a*). When the parasite has filled the whole body of its host, destroying the ovary in the process, it is ready for sporulation. The process of sporulation usually takes place in the evening and is over in less than two hours. The final products are small dinospores, complete with girdle, sulcus and two flagella, and set all over with minute trichites (Fig. 53*b*). The dinospores become active inside the host and leave by a split in the exoskeleton. Chatton has described several types of dinospore from different species of copepod.

Apstein has not described *Syndinium* unless the concretions of his No. 18 belong to that parasite. In Jepps' specimens from the Clyde it occurred rarely and the few which were obtained were taken in early spring.

These last two parasites are, from the form of their spores, clearly dinoflagellate; the following two are of doubtful systematic position but may be related to this group.

Paradinium (Fig. 54). This is the most abundant parasite in the Clyde sea area and Jepps has given a detailed description of it (1937*a*). She is inclined to think it more closely related to the Mycetozoa than to the dinoflagellates although in many ways it resembles *Syndinium* closely. Chatton described it from other copepods in the Mediterranean.

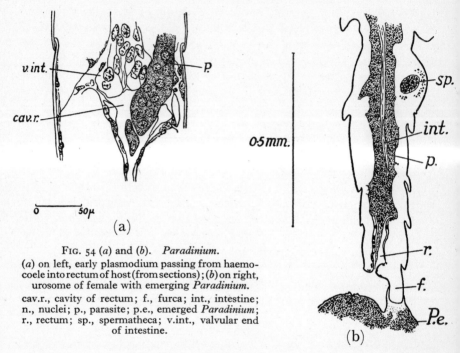

FIG. 54 (*a*) and (*b*).   *Paradinium.*

(*a*) on left, early plasmodium passing from haemo-coele into rectum of host (from sections); (*b*) on right, urosome of female with emerging *Paradinium.*

cav.r., cavity of rectum; f., furca; int., intestine; n., nuclei; p., parasite; p.e., emerged *Paradinium*; r., rectum; sp., spermatheca; v.int., valvular end of intestine.

The earliest stage seen is a delicate reticulum formed of spindle-shaped bodies united by strands of protoplasm. This soon thickens and spreads throughout the *Calanus* in thin sheets on the body walls and in thicker orange masses in the open cavities (Fig. 54*a*). The reticular spaces eventually fill up and all the body spaces of the host are filled with the mass. There then appear a large number of concretions of variable size formed of fatty material. After their deposition sporulation begins but immediately before it happens the concretions disappear again which indicates that they form a reserve material which is rapidly modified for use during sporulation. About this time two other cytoplasmic inclusions appear in numbers, large eosinophil bodies often seen in the spaces left by the vanished concretions and small crystalline rods 1-2μ long which appear in enormous numbers and are later seen in the tails of the swarm spores. A wave of nuclear division, suggestive of a meiotic division then sweeps over the plasmodium. The whole mass then flows backwards actively, makes its way into the gut and emerges by the anus (Fig. 54*b*). For a while the *Calanus* swims about with this orange mass attached to its urosome. According to Chatton the outside of the mass is sticky and has a membranous wall. An hour or so after extrusion the nuclei begin to divide, the cytoplasm segments and the whole mass divides into swarm spores 8-10 μ long with two flagella, one

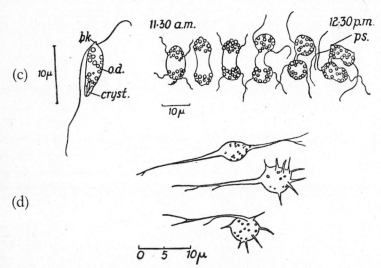

FIG. 54 (*c*) and (*d*).   *Paradinium.*
(*c*) division of extruded parasite to form bodonispores;
(*d*) amoebiform bodies sketched from life.
bk., beak; cryst., crystalloids; o.d., oil drops; ps., pseudopodium like projection.

leading and one trailing (Fig. 54*c*). The spores contain numerous yellow droplets and some of the crystalline rods already mentioned. There is a 'beak' at the anterior end of the spore and a suggestion of a groove under it but they do not much resemble the typical dinospores of *Syndinium*.

This process sometimes goes on inside the body of the host, even to the production of swarm spores. Abnormal and probably degenerating nuclei are common in the plasmodium particularly if sporulation is interrupted. The fate of the spores is not certainly known but on one occasion a *Calanus,* in a vessel containing three more which had just sporulated, was clustered over with the remains of swarm spores as well as with peculiar amoeboid bodies which were gliding over the carapace and may have been derived from spores (Fig. 54*d*).

The parasite leaves its host almost completely and although in the laboratory the latter invariably dies within a few days, Jepps thinks that under natural conditions it may occasionally recover.

Ellobiopsis chattoni (Fig. 55). This is a parasite widely distributed on *Calanus* from regions as far apart as the Arctic and the Mediterranean. The first was recorded by T. Scott (1897) from Loch Fyne in the Clyde area. Its systematic position is still uncertain. Chatton included it, but with some doubts, among the dinoflagellates, but although Jepps has described the beginning of sporulation, the spores themselves have not been seen. There are several similar parasites on other animals and in one of them, *Parallobiopsis*, Hovasse (1925) has described flagellispores and has therefore said that the group belongs to some other division of the flagellates than the dinoflagellates. Boschma (1949) however who recently reviewed the whole group thinks that *Ellobiopsis* is not closely related to *Parallobiopsis* and that its systematic position is still uncertain. Jepps is inclined to put it among the fungi.

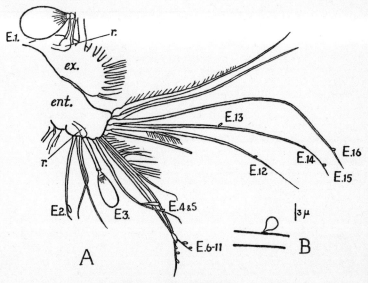

FIG. 55 (*a*). *Ellobiopsis*.
A, maxillule of *Calanus* with 16 *Ellobiopsis*, (E, 1-16), B, E 13 more highly magnified.
ent., endopod; ex., exopod; r., 'root' of parasite.

The earliest stages have been described by Jepps as small oval bodies no more than 3 μ long attached to the mouth parts (Fig. 55*a*). As many as 16, ranging from 3-70 μ in length were found on one *Calanus* maxillule. Since a *Calanus* is never heavily infested with large specimens most of them must die off at an early stage. The external part grows to a length of

700 μ with a diameter of 350 μ and consists of an oval or club-shaped test (Fig. 55b) containing a dark granular mass. There is a stalk piercing the

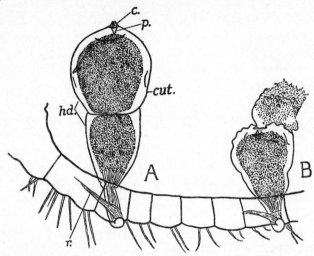

FIG. 55 (b). *Ellobiopsis* right antennule with two *Ellobiopsis*, A and B.
c., apical cone; cut., cuticle of parasite; hd., 'head'; p., plug; r., 'root'.

cuticle of the host which contains a bundle of fibres passing from the body of the parasite, through a hole in the cuticle much narrower than the stalk, into the limb of the host. Inside the limb the fibre bundle is covered with a sheath which soon dwindles away and the 'root' passes along the limb, always towards the body of the *Calanus*.

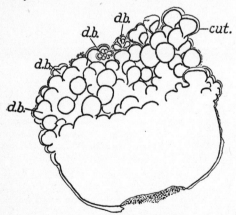

FIG. 55 (c). Upper half of an *Ellobiopsis* forming spores.
cut., cuticle; d.b., dividing bud.

By the time the external part of the parasite has reached a length of 200-300 μ it has divided into two segments, a proximal pear-shaped trophomere, and a rounded distal gonomere (Fig. 55b). The trophomere is usually smaller but sometimes larger than the gonomere.

Some kind of sporulation now takes place in the gonomere. The divisions begin at the free surface, first into buds about 30 μ in diameter, each of which then undergoes a series of fissions into little collections of successively smaller buds, the smallest being 3-4 μ across (Fig. 55c). Their nuclei could not be seen. Even in young stages there is no sign of large nuclear structures and the head seems to contain only vast numbers of very small nuclei about 2 μ in diameter. The trophomere also contains small nuclei which have been seen in a state of division.

Hovasse (1951) observed sporulation in a related species *E. fagei*; the spores were released in small masses and at that stage had no flagella.

After sporulation has taken place it is possible that a new gonomere is divided off to repeat the process. In related forms, such as *Amallocystis* on Euphausids, one trophomere may carry a string of several gonomeres. In *Amallocystis* the organ of attachment, too, is more elaborate with a sieve plate through which long root-like processes pass into the ovary of the host. The simple organ of *Ellobiopsis* must also absorb food from the host for in female *Calanus* thus infected the ovaries do not develop normally. *Ellobiopsis* is more common in summer than in winter.

Sporozoa

Gregarines (Fig. 56). Although the gregarines in *Calanus* have been known for a long time they have not yet been named, nor is anything known of their life history. They are found in the gut, more commonly in summer than in winter, and are simple cylindrical bodies with one end rounded and the other differentiated in various ways, being sometimes hollowed out, sometimes having a short protruding mobile process. They are frequently seen in chains of two or occasionally three with the differentiated end of one fitting over the rounded end of the next. The rounded end of a gregarine was once seen to have attached to it not only its own 'tail' but also those of a single one and of a chain of two (Fig. 56). An individual gregarine may reach a length of over 1 mm, but they are usually much smaller. They have not been seen attached to the gut wall but usually lie loose in its lumen; Jepps has seen a ball of them expelled through the anus. They seem to have no injurious effect on their host.

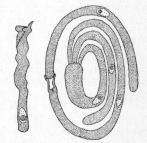

Fig. 56. Gregarines from the gut of a *Calanus*, drawn from life.

Ciliata

Chattonella calani Jepps (Figs. 57 and 58). We owe our knowledge of the structure of this little ciliate to Jepps (1937a) who studied it in specimens from the Clyde sea area. It had already been mentioned by Apstein as occurring in *Calanus* from the North Sea and is possibly the form described by Krøyer (1848) on the mouth parts of *C. hyperboreus*. It is more common in autumn and winter than in summer and the proportion of infected *Calanus* may be high—up to 50% or more of females and Stage V. Few males and no early stages have been seen infected.

The ciliates are found clustered at the base of the maxilla and rarely anywhere else (Fig. 57). One, two, or any number up to twenty may form the group and they are in constant movement. Their thick covering of cilia produces a shimmering effect as their bodies tumble about a fixed point. A mucus is secreted to help in their attachment. The rounded body, 30-60 μ long, is slightly flattened in one plane; the cilia are longer on an oval area, the sole, which lies next the maxilla and can be stretched out at one end into a tail (Fig. 58A-E). Some of the longer cilia on the tail are held stiffly as though attached. Besides these there are some long motile cilia leading into a depression at the opposite end of the sole which may be a mouth. No food however was seen to go into this. The cytoplasm is filled with shining granules, there is a contractile vacuole, the macronucleus is elongated and the micronucleus spherical.

Among these ciliates are often seen smaller flattened transparent forms, up to 20 μ long, ciliated on the ventral side only, which run about over the *Chattonella* and their host (Fig. 58F-H). These may be young forms or they may be independent organisms.

Chattonella was not seen to take any food but Jepps points out that the position it has chosen is close to the opening of the maxillary gland and that this may be the attraction. Although it seems to be commensal rather than parasitic yet it has the same distribution among the developmental stages as do the true parasites. This, however, may be because of the longer life of the female and Stage V.

Chatton and Lwoff (1935) have described a number of apostomatous ciliates, several of which spend part of their life in cysts (phorontes) attached to the exoskeleton of copepods. Jepps described some North Sea *Calanus* which had several of these phorontes scattered over their ventral surface. Sewell (1951) has described several types of cyst attached to the setae of the antennules and mouth parts of various copepods, and similar cysts have been seen on *Calanus* from near Bear Island. They are small oval bodies with a stalk attached at or near one end.

Apstein lists a ciliate which was so numerous that it partly covered the copepods (*Calanus* and others) but he gives no drawings and it has not been recognized since. Krøyer (1848), too, mentions masses of 'eggs of parasites' stuck on the back of *C. hyperboreus*. It seems possible that these may also have been phorontes.

Many of these phorontes hatch out when their crustacean host moults and then live and grow in the exuviae, so that they are commensal rather than parasitic. Ciliates have however, also been described living in the coelomic cavity of copepods. Apstein figures one from *Calanus*, about 80 μ long with a small round nucleus.

In the neighbourhood of Tromsø, in Northern Norway, a few *Calanus* were found parasitized by a different ciliate. The body of the host was filled with a dark mass, so dense that the structure could not be made out but the more open spaces, e.g. the abdomen, antennules and other limbs, were full of small ciliates moving rapidly backwards and forwards. The *Calanus* were lively when caught but did not survive long in the laboratory. The ciliates were about 60 μ long and 44 μ wide. In stained specimens the macronucleus is seen in the form of a mesh work lying close to the surface of the cell. This type of nucleus is characteristic of some of the apostomatous ciliates described by Chatton and Lwoff (although not of those living on copepods), but so far none has been found living in the coelomic cavity of their crustacean hosts. In several however the life history is not fully known.

Jepps mentions having seen an occasional suctorian, *Ephelota*. These however can even less than *Chattonella* be considered as parasites.

Nematoda

Contracaecum sp. (Fig. 59) occurs singly in the body cavity and is found in *Sagitta* as well as in *Calanus*. The earliest stage seen was only about 100-200 μ long and was wriggling actively round about the oesophagus, but all sizes are found up to those which are much longer than the *Calanus* which contains them and have to lie coiled up in the body cavity (Fig. 59a). Their growth is fairly rapid. In a very immature female *Calanus*, kept in the laboratory at Millport from 16th February, a small nematode was first noticed on the 21st, and by 6th March had grown large. Judging from this one, the largest specimens must have been in the *Calanus* for at least four or five weeks but the rapidity of growth will probably depend on the nutrition of the host. The *Calanus* does not turn red and the gonad rarely develops, although occasionally a female matures sufficiently to lay eggs. Apstein mentions a nematode occurring in *Calanus*, *Euchaeta* and *Sagitta*.

Trematoda

A *Hemiurus* sp. occurs rarely and singly in *Calanus* and other copepods and a trematode parasite is listed also by Apstein. The most brilliantly red *Calanus* are usually those containing a trematode.

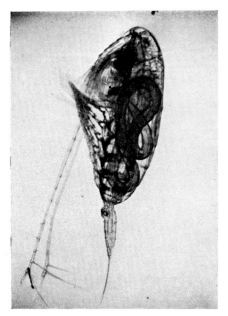
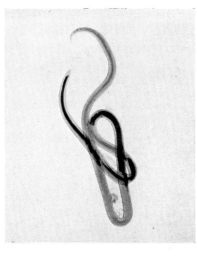

a   b

FIG. 59.   Nematodes.

(a) living *Calanus* containing a large nematode.
(b) nematode (6.1 mm long) removed from a *Calanus* and stained.

FIG. 60.   Tetraphyllid larvae, fixed and
stained, from the body cavity of a
Calanus ($\times$ 100).

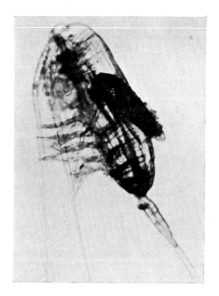

FIG. 61.   Late Microniscus larva of an
epicarid isopod, attached to *Calanus*
(×20).

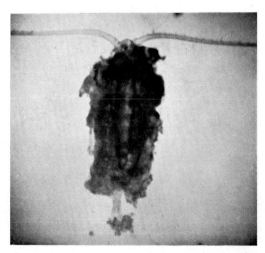

FIG. 62.   Living *Calanus* covered with a surface
growth of unidentified organisms.

Cestoda

Two types of cestode larva occur, a cyclophyllid and a tetraphyllid (Fig. 60). The first was mentioned by Apstein who counted 2600 individuals in a single *Calanus*. Tetraphyllids are less numerous and there are not usually more than a few hundred in a *Calanus*. It is extraordinary that such numbers should occur in one host and it is almost impossible that they should have been ingested individually. The late Professor J. S. Dunkerly who first studied these cestode larvae, particularly the tetraphyllid, came to the conclusion that some form of multiplication took place inside the host. He found plasmodia without definite cell walls but with nuclei resembling those of the cestode larvae, which sometimes seemed to be dividing. He suggested that when the embryo emerged from the egg in the gut of the *Calanus* it made its way into the haemocoele of the host and formed an embryonic mass, budding off numerous small bodies which grew into fully developed larvae. He thought he recognized in the Clyde *Calanus* three distinct forms of tetraphyllid larvae, one a tetrarhynch. His work has not been published.

Jepps (1937*b*) found in some of the infected *Calanus* plasmodial masses which were like those of *Ichthyosporidium* except that they writhed about actively. She identified them from their cytological structure as developing cestodes and was able also to identify Asptein's Nos. 6, 7 and 8 as such developmental forms.

The larval development of these cestodes is therefore something like that of *Urocystis prolifer* in *Glomeris marginata* (Coleoptera) described by Joyeux (1922). Tetraphyllid cestodes usually have an elasmobranch fish as the final host but we know too little about the cestode parasites of elasmobranchs in the Clyde to make a guess at the destination of those inhabiting *Calanus*.

Crustacea

The Microniscus (Fig. 61) is a larval stage in the development of epicarid isopods, is parasitic on copepods and is found occasionally on *Calanus*. There is some doubt about how far these larvae are truly parasitic; they have mouth parts adapted for piercing and Reverberi and Pitotti (1943) think that they pierce the host's chitin and so nourish themselves. In some of the parasitized Clyde *Calanus* the ovary seemed to be undeveloped but further observation is needed on this point. Dr R. B. Pike (personal communication) has watched the Microniscus larvae attaching themselves to *Calanus*. They frequently first catch on to the appendages and cling there, gradually working their way up on to the body, where they settle down. Those that do not succeed in reaching the body are soon thrown off. He thinks too that although the earliest Microniscus stage is not para-

L

sitic, after its first moult it pierces the chitin of the host and remains attached in that way until development is complete.

Only a few of the parasites listed above are quite without visible effect on the *Calanus*. These are gregarines, *Chattonella* and possibly Microniscus, although the second can hardly be considered as a true parasite. All the rest prevent the normal development of the gonad. Apart from the longer life of the female one of the reasons why this is the stage most often parasitized may be that there is in it a rapid and continuous supply of nutriment to the ovaries. The Stage V (apart from the over-wintering brood) eat as much as females although in them the reproductive organs are not developing to the same extent and the excess may be stored as oil; the males eat less and so parasites will presumably find a less favourable environment.

It will be noticed that of all the parasites described the method of infection is known, or even surmised, in only two, *Paradinium* and Microniscus. In several ingress is doubtless by the mouth, along with the food. Nor except for Microniscus is the complete history of any of these parasites known, although several of them have other hosts.

It is an interesting fact that the parasites vary greatly from year to year in their incidence. Thus cestode larvae when first noticed in the Clyde sea area in 1924 were rare, tetraphyllids much rarer than cyclophyllids. By about 1930 tetraphyllids had become more numerous and in 1932 and 1933 cyclophyllids were very rare and tetraphyllids comparatively common. Since then both have become rare again. *Ellobiopsis* is a summer form and was very common in the summers of 1931 and 1932. Nematodes were rare before 1933, but were comparatively common then and in 1951. The parasite which occurs most frequently is *Paradinium* and there are few large catches of *Calanus* without a number containing this form.

Apart from parasites there are various ills which beset the *Calanus* especially in the laboratory. Jepps says that disorders of the female reproductive system are not uncommon and described large eggs which have broken loose into the body cavity and are 'swept round in the circulation, being squeezed through the narrow channels and shot across the wide open spaces so that they look like some very active independent organism'.

In *Calanus* kept for long in the laboratory there tend to develop surface growths (Fig. 62) in the form of a dense mat of minute unidentified organisms probably largely bacterial. Sometimes the growth envelops the whole body and the *Calanus* may live like this for some weeks though it becomes very sluggish. Bacterial infections develop in the gut also and these kill the *Calanus* very rapidly. Sometimes the oil in the oil sac goes opaque and this too is usually a sign of approaching death.

CHAPTER XI

CALANUS IN RELATION TO ITS ENVIRONMENT

THE distribution of *Calanus* in the sea is some guide to the influence of its inanimate environment, and our knowledge has been supplemented by studies in the laboratory. Its relations to the animate environment are of economic importance because it acts as a link between the phytoplankton on the one hand and the pelagic carnivores on the other, turning the phytoplankton into food palatable to whales and to many species of fish.

INANIMATE ENVIRONMENT

Its distribution from the Arctic to tropical waters shows that *Calanus* is able to tolerate temperatures from below 0°C up to about 30°C. The lower limit is very close to the temperature at which sea water freezes. Laboratory tests to find the upper limit have been made by Huntsman and Sparks (1925) and Marshall, Nicholls and Orr (1935). The former found a limit between 26·5 and 29·5°C, the latter a limit of 25-27°C. The slight discrepancy may be owing to the different rate of rise of temperature in the two series of experiments; Huntsman and Sparks raised the temperature more quickly than did Marshall, Nicholls and Orr. The latter also found that male and female *Calanus* were less resistant to high temperatures than Stage V and that the lethal temperature was higher in summer than in winter. This suggests that the ability to withstand temperature changes may depend on the temperature conditions under which the *Calanus* have developed. Brown (1929) for example found that in cladocerans, northern species and those with spring and autumn maxima have a lower lethal temperature than southern species and those with summer maxima. It has been shown (Fox, 1937; Edwards and Irving, 1943*a* and *b*) that a similar adaptation occurs in the respiration of other species occurring in waters of different temperatures. Temperature also affects the rate of heart beat in *Calanus* (Harvey, 1930). It rises from about 200 beats per minute at 5·5°C to 350 beats at 16°C.

The effect of temperature on size has already been discussed (p. 81 *et seq.*).

The influence of salinity on the distribution of *Calanus* may be important. Farran (1911) states that it is abundant only when the salinity of the sea is 35·3⁰/₀₀ or less. Laboratory experiments on the effect of changes of salinity on the survival of *Calanus* (Marshall, Nicholls and Orr, 1935) show that sudden changes are lethal. *Calanus* can however become acclimatized to quite low salinities if the changes are made gradually. They live apparently as well in water of a salinity of $27^0/_{00}$ as they do in oceanic sea water. They can become acclimatized to salinities as low as $12\text{-}17^0/_{00}$, though the respiration then shows a considerable decrease and the animals are sluggish. This faculty of acclimatization makes it surprising that they have not colonized the Baltic.

Calanus is moderately sensitive to a reduction in the oxygen content of its surroundings. High values for oxygen content such as are sometimes obtained in the sea during a diatom increase seem to have no effect and indeed raising the oxygen content to as much as three times the normal value in the sea had no effect on its survival or on its respiration. A reduction of oxygen content below normal may however prove fatal. In the laboratory at 15°C a reduction to about half (3·3 ml/l) was fatal to male and female *Calanus* in a few hours, though Stage V survived for a considerably longer time. At lower values the death rate was higher in Stage V as well as adults. The effect of lower temperature (5°C) is to lengthen the period of survival at low oxygen content. Lowered oxygen content also affects the respiration (see p. 117). In spite of these results *Calanus* in the sea is found in places where the oxygen content is low. Thus in fjords *Calanus* may be abundant in the deeper water where one might expect the low oxygen to have a harmful influence. As already mentioned *Calanus* has been found in the Black Sea at depths where the oxygen was below 1 ml/l. The factor of acclimatization may come in here too. The oxygen content is low only in a comparatively few special localities in the sea and it seems unlikely that for *Calanus* it has any important effect on distribution.

The changes in pH value in the sea are relatively small and are not likely to affect *Calanus*. This was confirmed in laboratory experiments in which it was found that changes greater than those found in the sea had no effect on survival or on respiration.

Light is certainly one of the most important factors in the life of a copepod yet it is the one whose effects are the most difficult to explain. This is no doubt partly because light conditions in the sea are very difficult to simulate in the laboratory and partly because most experiments on *Calanus* are impossible without first exposing them to light much stronger than they would meet in their natural environment. Few experimenters have taken so much trouble as Hardy and Paton (1947) in shielding their *Calanus* from light before starting an experiment, but in spite of this their results are not easy to interpret. Difficulties are also caused by the fact that reaction to light as shown by vertical migration varies from one developmental stage to another and in the same stage at different times

of year. It is unsafe to compare results of experiments from different
places unless the work has been done at a comparable time of year and on
animals comparable in development. The effect of light on the biology
of *Calanus* has already been discussed in Chapters VIII and IX.

Considering that exposure to sunlight is fatal to *Calanus* it is one of the
most surprising things in their life cycle that at some times of the year
they are found right at the surface in brilliant sunshine. Russell (1930*b*)
has suggested that when they come to the surface the fats in their body are
irradiated and vitamin A is formed. This suggestion is however not supported by the recent findings of Fisher *et al* (1952) that *Calanus* is always
poor in vitamins.

ANIMATE ENVIRONMENT

Relation to phytoplankton

The mutual influence of the copepods and the diatoms did not attract
much attention from early workers on plankton.

Damas in 1905 suggested that the swarms of developing *Calanus* in the
Norwegian Sea were responsible for the rapid disappearance of the masses
of diatoms present when the eggs were laid but it was not till 1934 that
Harvey took up the subject again and tried to give a quantitative meaning
to the relationship between copepods and phytoplankton. He found that
when the spring diatoms in the English Channel disappeared there were
still sufficient nutrient salts in the water to support their growth and the
time of their disappearance was marked by the development of large
numbers of 'small larvae', of which no doubt copepods were an important
part. When he calculated the total number of diatoms producible from
the total amount of phosphate used up it was greater than the number
observed and he took this to mean that the excess had been consumed
by animals. A more detailed study was made later (Harvey *et al.*, 1935;
Harvey, 1942); the animal plankton was estimated as well as the plant,
and the number of copepod faecal pellets was counted. It was found
that this last number was related to the number of diatoms rather than
to the number of copepods. It was noticed that when pellets were most
abundant they were green rather than brown, suggesting that the plants
had not been fully digested. Again the amount of plant production was
much greater when calculated from the amount of phosphate used up
than from the actual numbers seen and the disappearances of the diatoms
after increases could be correlated with the increases in zooplankton. It
was concluded that the amount of phytoplankton in the sea was controlled
mainly by the grazing of the zooplankton. There are places, e.g. the
Barents Sea, and Loch Striven in Scotland, where a large number of dead
diatoms is deposited on the bottom at the end of the spring diatom in-

crease. In the Barents Sea indeed the main bulk of the diatom mass is apparently untouched by the copepods, but in temperate waters generally it is probably true that most of the phytoplankton is eaten.

A bold attempt was made by Fleming (1939) to express the changes in the English Channel as a dynamic equilibrium, the quantity of phytoplankton depending on temperature, illumination and the supply of nutrient salts for its increase on the one hand and on the grazing of the zooplankton for its decrease on the other. In spite of a lack of data about the rate of division of diatoms under known conditions and the filtration rate of different copepods, the observed and the calculated productivity are close. It is interesting to find that, using the rate of filtration of about 3 ml per *Calanus* per day then supposed to be correct, the grazing population ought to have been higher than that found by Harvey *et al.* Using the more recent figure (Gauld, 1951) of 20 to 30 times this, the difficulty disappears. The removal of diatoms by herbivores offers too a possible explanation of the 'animal exclusion' hypothesis of Hardy (Hardy and Gunther, 1935; Bainbridge, 1953). Because of grazing the probability of a rich diatom and zooplankton population occurring together is low.

A broad development of Fleming's treatment has been made in a series of papers by Riley and his co-workers (1946, 1947, 1948, 1949) dealing at first with localized areas and later with the western North Atlantic as a whole. In a limited area the agreement between the calculated and observed total production has been remarkably close. It is seldom that sufficient data are available for estimates to be made of the total production in wider areas but in the western North Atlantic the discrepancy between the observed and the calculated production of phytoplankton and zooplankton averages about 25%. These studies emphasize the lack of adequate data on the physiology of diatoms and zooplankton.

The zoo- and phytoplankton are often separated either horizontally or vertically, but there are also areas where rich zoo- and phytoplankton are found together. Steemann Nielsen (1937) has described such concentrations in areas where upwelling is going on. He also points out that the separation of zoo- and phytoplankton can be largely explained by the different rates at which they develop. An increase in diatoms may for example start off a brood of copepods but by the time these have developed the diatom increase will be over, partly because of the depletion of nutrients and partly because of grazing. Occasionally there is an intense development of phytoplankton injurious to other animals, e.g. the mass production of dinoflagellates in 'red water' which kills off fish (Gunter *et al.*, 1948), and the high concentration of flagellates which causes injury to oysters in oyster polls (Gaarder, 1932).

A general view of the distribution of *Calanus finmarchicus* shows that it

has a very wide range and, within this, is most abundant where the productivity of the sea is greatest, i.e. where there are abundant plant nutrients.
In temperate regions there is a rich supply of food in spring and autumn
and *Calanus* is common throughout north temperate waters, being often
the dominant organism, if we consider biomass,* even if not numerically.
In the Arctic (Jaschnov, 1939) on the other hand it is probably the dominant zooplankton organism numerically although the euphausids *Meganyctiphanes* and *Thysanoessa* may at times be more important in biomass. It
is absent in the Antarctic where its place is taken by other *Calanus* spp.
and where the dominant organism is *Euphausia superba*.

In Arctic regions there is abundant plant food during the summer but
during the winter it is very scarce and it is difficult to understand how the
Calanus survive in numbers sufficient to produce the enormous summer
broods. The over-wintering stock declines continuously in numbers
throughout the autumn and winter. The animals must depend partly on
their fat reserves, and they may live partly by eating each other (Digby,
1954). There are also indications from experimental work (done when
Stage V made up the stock) that metabolism is lowered in the over-wintering population. According to accounts of catches made in the Arctic winter
(Hjort, 1933; Manteufel, 1941) it is difficult to find even a few specimens of
Calanus then, yet there is only one generation a year and these solitary specimens are apparently the sole parents of the enormous swarms which are
found in summer. Judging from recent work (Marshall and Orr, 1952) it is
unlikely that the females will lay an average of as much as 400 eggs each,
yet the summer swarms described seem to be far more than 200 times the
winter numbers, and this would take no account of mortality during
development. It may be that they are much more evenly distributed in
winter or that they are living below the depths sampled by Hjort and
Manteufel. Some copepods (e.g. *Calanopia* in St. Georges Harbour,
Bermuda; Clarke, 1934*b*) are even known to bury themselves in the mud
during the day. The same sort of discrepancy between winter and spring
or summer numbers appears sometimes in temperate waters but can be
explained in a different way (see p. 66). In any case, there is more than
one generation there and it is not always the first which produces the
maximum numbers.

Calanus as a food

The fate of *Calanus* in the sea has attracted attention hitherto only in
so far as it forms an important food for larger animals of economic importance. Since in the laboratory under conditions which must be in many
ways much less favourable than in the open sea, *Calanus* can be kept alive

* i.e. the weight of organisms per unit of volume or under unit area of the sea surface.

for several months, we must conclude that in nature the periodic reduction in the stock of *Calanus* must be largely because of natural enemies. In British waters *Calanus* remains as Stage V for five or six months from autumn till mid-winter and during the Arctic winter they must remain in the earlier stages for even longer.

A large number of plankton animals prey on *Calanus* (Lebour, 1922, 1923). Among these is the arrow worm *Sagitta* which sometimes appears in large numbers in plankton hauls. Since its digestion is, as in most transparent animals, very rapid, most have empty guts; in those with recognizable food, *Calanus* is commonly present (Wilson, 1932, p. 26).

The ctenophores which develop in large numbers in late spring and in early summer just when the *Calanus* population is rich are very destructive. Bigelow (1926) noted that it was common to find them packed with copepods, euphausids and young fishes and that when they were abundant the smaller plankton animals were largely exterminated. Lebour (1923) and Russell (1934b) also drew attention to the destruction by them of the animal plankton. In the Barents Sea they appear in large numbers in summer and according to Manteufel (1941) when they are abundant *Calanus* is scarce and *vice versa*. In some years owing to abnormally high temperatures their increase takes place earlier than usual, when 'red' *Calanus* are swarming at the surface, and they destroy so many that the herring fishery may be a failure. Medusae are also very destructive of *Calanus*. Some of the large copepods (e.g. *Euchaeta* and *Anomalocera*) and some of the euphausids are also carnivorous and may capture *Calanus*. Apart from those mentioned above, however, there appear to be few other invertebrates which take them on a large scale.

Calanus is very important as a food for fish, especially for pelagic fish. The young of very many species feed on it and even small flatfish which normally feed on the bottom can capture *Calanus*. It may also form a link in the food chain of fish which do not feed exclusively on plankton. For example Hardy (1924) has shown that *Ammodytes* is a very important food of the herring in the North Sea. Bogorov, Manteufel and Packova (1939) have shown that in the Arctic *Ammodytes* in turn feeds largely on *Calanus* (70% by weight).

Of the different pelagic fishes which eat *Calanus*, the herring is the most abundant and for this reason the relation between *Calanus* and the herring has been most closely studied. Most of the observations have been made on adult herring taken from commercial catches, but some results are also available for young herring (Lebour, 1921, 1924; Hardy, 1924; Ogilvie, 1927; Marshall, Nicholls and Orr, 1937, 1939). *Calanus* eggs have been found in the gut of larvae four weeks old and 18 mm long, but *Calanus* nauplii have been found even in herring 14 mm long, only a week after hatching. A Stage I copepodite has been found in a herring of 16·5 mm, 6 Stage I in a herring of 23 mm; Stages IV and V were found in herring of 33 mm and adults in herring from 35 mm upwards.

For pre-metamorphosis herring the food must be abundant in the water (Soleim, 1942) and it must be of a size suitable for the herring to catch. Comparisons with townettings taken at the same time showed that the young herring during their first month were limited in their diet by the size of their food. Many of the small herring contain little or no food and Hardy (1924) has suggested that on capture they eject it. This is supported by the fact that often there are swellings in the empty gut as though it had recently contained food.

When young herring reach a length of about 40 mm there is a big increase in the amount of food they take. In the Clyde sea area *Calanus*, although not the most numerous, was the most important copepod owing to its large size. On one occasion an average of nearly 2,000 *Calanus* was found in the gut of small herring of 150 mm length. Hardy (1924), Jespersen (1928) and Ogilvie (1927) also found that copepods were the chief part of the diet of young herring, but *Calanus* was not so important in the North Sea as in the Clyde sea area.

One would expect the gut contents of the herring to reflect the plankton of the water in which they are caught. In the Clyde area they agreed in so far as the gut contents were low in winter when the plankton was poor and high in spring and summer when plankton was rich; no closer relationship could be made out. Possibly this was because the herring were caught as they came inshore at dusk and had therefore been feeding in a different locality from where the plankton hauls were taken.

Along with euphausids, *Calanus* forms the food of the small herring which make an important fishery in the Passamaquoddy region of southern New Brunswick (Battle *et al.*, 1936). There is there a close correlation between the fatness of the herring and the food near the surface. There is no correlation between the fatness and the total amount of food in different areas of this region.

Diurnal fluctuations in the feeding of young herring have been studied by several workers. Jespersen (1928) found that feeding decreased during the night and Mužinić (1931) found that feeding was at its maximum from 5-9 p.m. after which it slackened off till 4 or 5 a.m. when there was a slight increase. Similar results have been obtained in the Clyde area. According to Battle *et al.* young herring need a good light to feed by and though moonlight is bright enough, starlight is not.

For the adult herring which make up the commercial shoals it has long been recognized that *Calanus* is one of the most important foods (Hardy, 1924; Savage, 1931; Jespersen, 1932; Ogilvie, 1934; Wailes,

1936; Radovich, 1952). Mention has already been made of the importance of the 'red' *Calanus* in the Arctic and on the northern coast of Norway. Various other authors refer to the importance of copepods without specifying the species eaten. For the west of Scotland, Brook (1886) reported on the importance of *Calanus* in summer as a herring food in Loch Fyne. Brook and Calderwood (1886) concluded that for the herring *Calanus* was the most important copepod on both the east and west coast of Britain though on the east it was not quite so dominant as on the west. In the

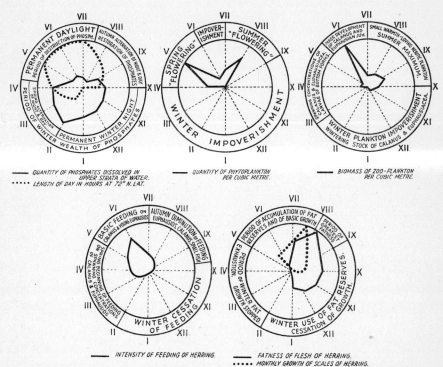

FIG. 63.   The food chains in the Barents Sea (after Manteufel).

Barents Sea the mass development of *Calanus* in summer provides the food for the herring shoals where there is a considerable fishery. The Pacific herring also, *Clupea pallasii*, feeds largely on copepods which form its chief food especially in spring. Calanoids are the most important copepods in the diet, *Calanus finmarchicus* and *C. tonsus* being abundant.

It is because it is one of the most widely spread, most abundant and largest of copepods that *Calanus* is so common a food of pelagic fish. It is not surprising therefore that efforts have been made to locate shoals of fish by the presence or absence of *Calanus* in the water. A simple zooplankton sampler suitable for use by fishing boats was devised by Hardy (1936), and by means of it and more elaborate samplers, an attempt has been made to relate the zooplankton to herring catches in the North Sea. There was usually a positive correlation; negative correlations were thought to be caused by the approach of the spawning season. The highest catches were likely to be found in water rich in zooplankton.

By using a sensitive echo-sounder Cushing (1952) has shown that there is a close correspondence during the feeding season between the presence of herring shoals and rich patches of *Calanus* in the North Sea. He thinks that so long as the grazing intensity of the herring is less than the rate of reproduction of the *Calanus*, aggregation of the herring will occur and herring and *Calanus* patches will coincide.

For the herring fisheries of the Barents Sea, Manteufel (1941) has examined the relation between the zooplankton and the herring (Fig. 63). There in winter the herring shoals keep to the same deep levels as the winter stock of *Calanus* and so their chances of finding food are greater than in the upper strata. This agrees with the observation that though herring caught in the winter are in poor condition, those caught in deep water are in better condition than those from the upper strata. In spring *Calanus* rise to the surface to form pre-spawning concentrations and about the same time the spring diatom increase begins at the surface. The herring also rise from the deep water then, but according to Manteufel the diatoms prevent their reaching the main concentrations of *Calanus* and they feed on the descending spent adults. When *Calanus* copepodites II and III become abundant there is a slight positive correlation with herring catches. With the disappearance of the diatom increase and the development of the *Calanus* into 'red' Stages III to V in masses at the surface, the herring shoals break up to feed and there is no correlation between catches of *Calanus* and herring. Later in July they gather into large commercial shoals still feeding intensively and there is a strong positive correlation between *Calanus* and herring. Later still when the herring become fat and the stock of *Calanus* is reduced by their depredations and those of other enemies, the correlation becomes negative.

The capture of copepods by fish has been observed on a few occasions in the sea and in the laboratory. The earlier workers considered that plankton-feeding fish were similar to whales and merely filtered water rich in plankton without making any selection or showing any definite act of capture. Scott (1887) and Ehrenbaum (see Bullen, 1908, 1912) on the other hand watched herring feeding in aquaria and concluded that they prey on plankton by selection. Damant (1921) and Hardy (1924) reached the same conclusion, the former by watching mackerel feeding in the sea while he was suspended in a diving suit and the latter by an analysis of the stomach contents of herring and a comparison of this with the plankton in the sea water in which they were caught. Hardy also watched herring feeding on various kinds of food in an aquarium and concluded that they make a definite act of capture and can select their food.

While *Calanus* are rich at the surface in spring in the Clyde area, it is easy to observe their capture in the sea by young saithe (*Gadus virens*) which dart at each individual *Calanus*. In the aquarium many species of young and adult fish feed greedily when *Calanus* are introduced. Most succeed easily in catching *Calanus*, which presumably are more readily visible to fish than when in the sea, but sometimes the *Calanus* shows strong escape reactions just as it does in the laboratory when one tries to capture it with a pipette. The escape reactions may be small darts in any direction away from the fish but may occasionally be a zigzag flight of a foot or so or the *Calanus* may whirl round rapidly in a small circle for a few seconds. The capture of copepods by larval herring has been described by Soleim (1942). According to him if the larval herring fails to capture the copepod at its first one or two attempts, it gives up and dies.

The feeding of herring in the sea has not been directly observed but Wailes (1936) suggests that since purse-seined herring have seldom any food in their gut, they probably do not feed while in compact shoals. This is supported by the detailed observations of the feeding of herring by Battle *et al.* (1936). They kept herring in tanks lit only by artificial light. Normally the herring swam as a shoal but when *Calanus* were added to the tank to an average of 8·3 per l 'the fish in a few minutes broke ranks, began independent rapid movements, occasionally breaking the surface. They concentrated where the *Calanus* were most abundant.' In capturing a *Calanus*, the herring turned partly on its side. The herring seemed to see the *Calanus* when it came between the light source and its own eye. Feeding took place even in the comparatively weak light of a 15 watt bulb $7\frac{1}{2}$ m above the tank; when the light was brought nearer—to 1 m above the tank—the rate of feeding increased fivefold.

Some idea of the rate of capture of the *Calanus* and the effect of light is given by an experiment on herring 9-18 cm long in a concentration of *Calanus* of an average of 13·3 per l. After two hours in the dark the number of *Calanus* in the caecum was negligible, after an additional hour with two 15 watt bulbs $7\frac{1}{2}$ m above the tank, each herring had an average of 11 *Calanus* in the caecum; after a further hour with a single 15 watt bulb 1 m above the tank, each herring contained on an average 63 *Calanus* in the caecum.

Herring starved for two or three days fed readily when copepods were added to the tank and kept on feeding for about two hours before returning to the non-feeding close parallel formation. With a rich concentration of copepods the caecum was then usually well distended and its contents took about 15 hours to disappear. This clearing time was closely dependent on temperature and was 25 hours at 6°C and only 6 hours at 20°C.

At present we can explain only in part the relation between zooplankton and herring in the sea, but by studying the feeding of plankton-consuming fish in the aquarium it may be possible to understand more fully their behaviour and movements.

The whalebone whales are collectors of plankton on the largest scale, but unfortunately it is difficult to obtain quantitative data about the amount they consume, although from considerations of their bulk and their activity it is obvious that it must be very large. Their capacity for filtering plankton is limited by the size of the mouth and the speed with which the water can be filtered and the plankton swallowed. Dr F. C. Fraser has calculated (personal communication) that the mouth of a right whale has a capacity of 334 gallons (1·5 cubic metres), and that the corresponding figure for a rorqual with its distensible throat is 2-3 times as much. We should remember too that it is only during a part of the polar summer that a whalebone whale can obtain a rich plankton to supply its everyday needs, to build up a reserve for the winter and to provide for its young. During the polar winter food is comparatively scarce and in the tropics also there is not enough plankton to support them. Indeed when whales are caught in the tropics or during the polar winter they are invariably lean.

Even during the polar summer the plankton is not evenly distributed but occurs in patches. In the Antarctic, the chief food is *Euphausia superba*. In the Arctic it may be *Thysanoessa* or *Meganyctiphanes* or *Calanus finmarchicus* or a mixture. It has been shown (Hjort and Ruud, 1929; Hjort, 1933) that the Sei whale (*Balaenopterus borealis*) on the Norwegian coast lives chiefly on copepods, especially *Calanus finmarchicus*, and that there is a close correspondence between the catches of Sei whales and the richness of *Calanus* in the water. *Calanus* is much smaller than euphausids and possibly may escape capture by some species of whalebone whales. In the Sei whale, however, the baleen fringes are silky and closely knit (Norman and Fraser, 1937).

How a whale is able to locate the parts of the sea rich in zooplankton is unknown, but it is obvious that in the polar regions where richness of plankton often depends on a spawning concentration at the surface, the whale must somehow manage to be in the right place at the right time.

Observations on the actual feeding of whalebone whales are few. For the now almost extinct Greenland whale, Scoresby (1820) gives the following description: 'When the whale feeds, it swims with considerable velocity below the surface of the sea, with its jaws widely extended. A stream of water consequently enters its capacious mouth, and along with it, large quantities of water insects; the water escapes again at the sides; but the food is entangled and sifted, as it were, by the whalebone, which, from its compact arrangement, and the thick internal covering of hair, does not allow a particle the size of the smallest grain to escape.' The movement of the Sei whale while feeding has been described by Millais (1904-6) who says 'they cover the water very slowly, rolling in the usual fashion, without turning on the side'.

Apart from the whales the only other common large scale collector of plankton in the sea is the basking shark (*Cetorhinus maximus* (Gunner.)). Fisheries for this large shark exist in several places, the main object being to obtain the liver oil. Matthews and Parker (1950) have described the feeding habits. 'When feeding near the surface the basking shark swims along slowly at the rate of about 2 knots, with the mouth widely open, filtering the plankton out of the water by means of the gill rakers. The gill slits are widely opened and the whole pharyngeal region greatly expanded.' The area of the open mouth is at least half a square metre so that the volume filtered could be as large as 2000 cubic metres per hour. A colour photograph showing a basking shark feeding is given by Fraser Darling (1947).

Various biologists, impressed by the richness of some plankton hauls, have thought it possible to collect plankton directly for use as a food for stock or for man himself. Such suggestions have usually been made during times of emergency. Various methods for collection of the plankton, e.g. pumps, townets, or swing nets, have been proposed.

Tests were done by Clarke and Bishop (1948) using plankton nets from life-saving rafts; the results suggested that only a part of the food required by man could be obtained in this way. Their reports on the utilization of the food by rats were not encouraging. Heyerdahl (1950) gives an interesting description of the appearance and taste of plankton from the Humboldt current on the Kon-Tiki expedition. Hardy (1941, 1943-44) following up a suggestion by Sir John Graham Kerr made hauls for zooplankton on the west coast of Scotland in which *Calanus* predominated and made some analyses with a view to poultry feeding. Some fat is lost from *Calanus* on collecting and drying and even the small quantity which remains tends to go rancid.

Since there is a considerable wastage in the food chain—phytoplankton to zooplankton to fish—it might theoretically be desirable to catch the zooplankton directly. So far however the herring has proved a more efficient collector than man, and in polar regions it is at present more profitable to collect the plankton-feeding whales, than to collect the plankton itself.

REFERENCES

ADLER, G., and JESPERSEN, P., 1920. Variations saisonnières chez quelques copépodes planctoniques marins. *Medd. Komm. Havundersøg.*, Kbh., Ser. Plankton 2, No. 1, 46 pp.

AKEHURST, S. C., 1931. Observations on pond life, with special reference to the possible causation of swarming of phytoplankton. *J. R. micr. Soc.*, 51, 237-265.

APSTEIN, C., 1911. Parasiten von *Calanus finmarchicus*. *Wiss. Meeresuntersuch.*, Abt. Kiel, 13, 205-223.

ATKINS, W. R. G., and POOLE, H. H., 1933. The photo-electric measurement of the penetration of light of various wavelengths into the sea and the physiological bearing of the results. *Phil. Trans.*, B, 222, 129-164.

BAINBRIDGE, R., 1949. Movement of zooplankton in diatom gradients. *Nature*, 163, 910.

BAINBRIDGE, R., 1952. Underwater observations on the swimming of marine zooplankton. *J. Mar. biol. Ass. U.K.*, 31, 107-112.

BAINBRIDGE, R., 1953. Studies on the interrelationships of zooplankton and phytoplankton. *J. Mar. biol. Ass. U.K.*, 32, 385-447.

BAIRD, W., 1850. *Natural history of the British Entomostraca*. Ray Society, London.

BARNES, H., 1949. A statistical study of the variation in vertical plankton hauls, with special reference to the loss of the catch with divided hauls. *J. Mar. biol. Ass. U.K.*, 28, 429-446.

BARNES, H., and BARNES, M., 1953. Biometry of the copepod *Calanus finmarchicus* (Gunn.) in Stages V and VI. *J. Mar. biol. Ass. U.K.*, 32, 305-313.

BARNES, H., and MARSHALL, S. M., 1951. On the variability of replicate plankton samples and some applications of 'contagious' series to the statistical distribution of catches over restricted periods. *J. Mar. biol. Ass. U.K.*, 30, 233-263.

BATTLE, H. I., HUNTSMAN, A. G., JEFFERS, A. M., JEFFERS, G. W., JOHNSON, W. H., and McNAIRN, N. A., 1936. Fatness, digestion and food of Passamaquoddy young herring. *J. biol. Bd. Can.*, 2, 401-429.

BELLOC, G., FABRE, R., and SIMONNET, H., 1930. Contribution to the study of the biological activity of the sterols. Study of plankton sterols. *C. R. Acad. Sci.*, Paris, 191, No. 3, July.

BIGELOW, H. B., 1926. Plankton of the offshore waters of the Gulf of Maine. *Bull. U.S. Bur. Fish.*, 40, 1924, Pt. 2, 507 pp.

BIRGE, E. A., 1898. Plankton studies on Lake Mendota. II: The crustacea of the plankton. *Trans. Wis. Acad. Sci. Arts Lett.*, 11, 274-448.

BOECK, A., 1865. Oversigt over de ved Norges Kyster iagttagne Copepoder, henhørende til Calanidernes, Cyclopidernes, og Harpactidernes Familier. *Vid. Selskab. Forhandl.*, Christiania, 1864, 226-281.

BOGOROV, B. G., 1933. Modifications in the biomass of *Calanus finmarchicus* in accordance with its age (English summary). *Bull. océanogr. Inst.*, Moscow, 8, 1-16.

BOGOROV, B. G., 1934. Seasonal changes in biomass of *Calanus finmarchicus* in the Plymouth area. *J. Mar. biol. Ass. U.K.*, 19, 585-611.

BOGOROV, B. G., 1938. Diurnal vertical distribution of plankton under polar conditions. *Trans. Knipovich polyar Sci. Inst.*, 2, 93-107.

BOGOROV, B. G., 1946. Peculiarities of diurnal vertical migrations of zooplankton in polar seas. *J. Mar. Res.*, 6, 25-32.

BOGOROV, B. G., MANTEUFEL, B. P., and PACKOVA, A. E., 1939. Nutrition of the small sand eel (*Ammodytes tobianus*) in Murman waters. *Trans. Inst. Mar. Fish., U.S.S.R.*, 4, 355-366.

BOGOROV, B. G., and PREOBRAJENSKAYA, E., 1934. On the weight characteristics of the plankton organisms of the Barents Sea. II: Copepoda (English summary). *Bull. All-Union Sci. Res. Inst. Mar. Fish. and Oceanog.*, No. 2, 1-24.

BOND, R. M., 1934. Digestive enzymes of the pelagic copepod *Calanus finmarchicus*. *Biol. Bull. Wood's Hole*, 67, 461-465.

BORRADAILE, L. A., 1926. Notes upon crustacean limbs. *Ann. Mag. nat. Hist.*, S. 9, 17, 193-213.

BOSCHMA, H., 1949. Ellobiopsidae. *'Discovery' Rep.*, 25, 281-314.

BRADY, G. S., 1883. Report on the Copepoda obtained by H.M.S. *Challenger* during the years 1873-76. *Rep. Sci. Results 'Challenger'*, 8, 1-142.

BRODSKY, K. A., 1950. Calanoida of the far eastern and polar seas of the U.S.S.R. Fauna of the U.S.S.R., 35, 1-442. *Publ. Inst. Acad. Sci. Moscow.*

BROOK, G., 1886. Report on the herring fishery of Loch Fyne and the adjacent districts during 1885. *4th Ann. Rep. Fish. Bd Scot.*, 1885, 47-61.

BROOK, G., and CALDERWOOD, W. L., 1886. Report on the food of the herring. *4th Ann. Rep. Fish. Bd Scot.*, 1885, 102-128.

BROWN, L. A., 1929. The natural history of cladocerans in relation to temperature. I: Distribution and the temperature limits for vital activities. *Amer. Nat.*, 63, 248-264.

BULLEN, G. E., 1908. Plankton studies in relation to the western mackerel fishery. *J. Mar. biol. Ass. U.K.*, 8, 269-302.

BULLEN, G. E., 1912. Some notes upon the feeding habits of mackerel and certain clupeoids in the English Channel. *J. Mar. biol. Ass. U.K.*, 9, 394-403.

CANNON, H. G., 1928. On the feeding mechanism of the copepods *Calanus finmarchicus* and *Diaptomus gracilis*. *Brit. J. exp. Biol.*, 6, 131-144.

CATTLEY, J. G., 1948. Sex reversal in copepods. *Nature*, 161, 937.

CHATTON, E., 1920. Les péridiniens parasites; morphologie, reproduction, éthologie. *Arch. Zool. exp. gén.*, 59, 1-475.

CHATTON, E., and LWOFF, A., 1935. Les ciliés apostomes, morphologie, cytologie, éthologie, évolution, systematique. *Arch. Zool. exp. gén.*, 77, 1-453.

CLARKE, G. L., 1933. Diurnal migration of plankton in the Gulf of Maine and its correlation with changes in submarine illumination. *Biol. Bull. Wood's Hole*, 65, 402-436.

CLARKE, G. L., 1934a. Further observations on the diurnal migration of copepods in the Gulf of Maine. *Biol. Bull. Wood's Hole*, 67, 432-455.

CLARKE, G. L., 1934b. The diurnal migration of copepods in St. George's harbour, Bermuda. *Biol. Bull. Wood's Hole*, 67, 456-460.

CLARKE, G. L., 1934c. Factors affecting the vertical distribution of copepods. *Ecol. Monogr.*, 4, 530-540.

CLARKE, G. L., 1940. Comparative richness of zooplankton in coastal and offshore areas of the Atlantic. *Biol. Bull. Wood's Hole*, 78, 226-255.

CLARKE, G. L., and BISHOP, D. W., 1948. The nutritional value of marine zooplankton with a consideration of its use as an emergency food. *Ecology*, 29, 54-71.

CLARKE, G. L., and BONNET, D. D., 1939. The influence of temperature on the survival, growth, and respiration of *Calanus finmarchicus*. *Biol. Bull. Wood's Hole*, 76, 371-383.

CLARKE, G. L., and GELLIS, S. S., 1935. The nutrition of copepods in relation to the food cycle of the sea. *Biol. Bull. Wood's Hole*, 68, 231-246.

CLARKE, G. L., and ZINN, D. J., 1937. Seasonal production of zooplankton off Wood's Hole with special reference to *Calanus finmarchicus*. *Biol. Bull. Wood's Hole*, 73, 464-487.

CLAUS, C., 1863. *Die freilebenden Copepoden mit besonderer Berücksichtigung der Fauna Deutschlands, der Nordsee und des Mittelmeeres*. 230 pp. Leipzig.

CLAUS, C., 1881. Neue Beiträge zur Kenntniss der Copepoden unter besonderer Berücksichtigung Triester Fauna. *Arb. zool. Inst. Univ. Wien*, 3, 313-322.

COKER, R. E., 1933. Influence of temperature on size of freshwater copepods (*Cyclops*). *Int. Rev. Hydrobiol.*, 29, 406-436.

COLLIN, G., DRUMMOND, J. C., HILDITCH, T. P., and GUNTHER, E. R., 1934. Observations on the fatty constituents of marine plankton. II: General character of the plankton oils. *J. exp. Biol.*, 11, 198-202.

CURRIE, M. E., 1918. Exuviation and variation of plankton copepods with special reference to *Calanus finmarchicus*. *Proc. roy. Soc. Can.*, S. 3, 12, 207-233.

CUSHING, D. H., 1951. The vertical migration of planktonic crustacea. *Biol. Rev.*, 26, 158-192.

CUSHING, D. H., 1952. Echo surveys of fish. *J. Cons. int. Explor. Mer.*, 28, 45-60.

DAKIN, W. J., 1908. Notes on the alimentary canal and food of the Copepoda. *Int. Rev. Hydrobiol.*, 1, 772-782.

DAMANT, G. C. C., 1921. Illumination of plankton. *Nature*, 108, 42.

DAMAS, D., 1905. Notes biologiques sur les copépodes de la mer Norvégienne. *Publ. Circ. Cons. Explor. Mer.*, No. 22, 24 pp.

DANA, J. D., 1852, 1855. Crustacea. United States exploring expedition during the years 1838-1842 under the command of Charles Wilkes. 13, Pt. 2, 1-1618 Philadelphia 1852; *Atlas*, Plates 1-96, Philadelphia, 1855.

DARLING, F. FRASER, 1947. *Natural History of the Highlands and Islands*. London.

DIGBY, P. S. B., 1950. The biology of the small planktonic copepods of Plymouth. *J. Mar. biol. Ass. U.K.*, 29, 393-438.

DIGBY, P. S. B., 1954. The biology of the marine plankton copepods of Scoresby Sound, East Greenland. *J. Anim. Ecol.*, 23, 298-338.

M

DIXON, M., 1943. *Manometric methods*. Cambridge.

DRUMMOND, J. C., and GUNTHER, E. R., 1934. Observations on the fatty constituents of marine plankton. III: The vitamin A and D content of oils derived from plankton. *J. exp. Biol.*, 11, 203-209.

EDWARDS, G. A., and IRVING, L., 1943a. The influence of temperature and season upon the oxygen consumption of the sand crab, *Emerita talpoida*, Say. *J. cell. comp. Physiol.*, 21, 169-182.

EDWARDS, G. A., and IRVING, L., 1943b. The influence of season and temperature upon the oxygen consumption of the beach flea, *Talorchestia megalophthalma*. *J. cell. comp. Physiol.*, 21, 183-189.

ESTERLY, C. O., 1905. The pelagic copepoda of the San Diego region. *Univ. Calif. Publ. Zool.*, 2, 113-233.

ESTERLY, C. O., 1912. The occurrence and vertical distribution of the copepoda of the San Diego region with particular reference to nineteen species. *Univ. Calif. Publ. Zool.*, 9, 253-340.

ESTERLY, C. O., 1916. The feeding habits and food of pelagic copepods and the question of nutrition by organic substances in solution in the water. *Univ. Calif. Publ. Zool.*, 16, 171-184.

ESTERLY, C. O., 1919. Reactions of various plankton animals with reference to their diurnal migrations. *Univ. Calif. Publ. Zool.*, 19, 1-83.

ESTERLY, C. O., 1924. The free-swimming copepoda of San Francisco Bay. *Univ. Calif. Publ. Zool.*, 26, 81-129.

FARRAN, G. P., 1911. Copepoda. Résumé des observations sur le plankton des mers explorées par le Conseil pendant les années 1902-1908. *Bull. Crois. per. Explor. Mer, 2me partie*, 81-105.

FARRAN, G. P., 1927. The reproduction of *Calanus finmarchicus* off the south coast of Ireland. *J. Cons. int. Explor. Mer*, 2, 132-143.

FARRAN, G. P., 1929. Copepoda. Brit. Antarct. Terra Nova Exped. 1910, *Nat. Hist. Rep.*, 8, 203-306.

FARRAN, G. P., 1947. Vertical distribution of plankton (*Sagitta, Calanus* and *Metridia*) off the south coast of Ireland. *Proc. R. Irish Acad.*, 51, B, 121-136.

FILTEAU, G., 1947. Les copépodes marins de la Baie des Chaleurs. *Rapp. Sta. biol. St Laurent*, 6, 61-68.

FILTEAU, G., 1948. Recherches sur les copépodes marins de la Baie des Chaleurs. *Rapp. Sta. biol. St Laurent*, 7, 69-76.

FILTEAU, G., 1949. Les copépodes marins de la Baie des Chaleurs. *Rapp. Sta. biol. St. Laurent*, 8, 55-69.

FISH, C. J., 1936. The biology of *Calanus finmarchicus* in the Gulf of Maine and Bay of Fundy. *Biol. Bull. Wood's Hole*, 70, 118-141.

FISHER, L. R., KON, S. K., and THOMSON, S. Y., 1952. Vitamin A and carotenoids in certain invertebrates. I: Marine crustacea. *J. Mar. biol. Ass. U.K.*, 31, 229-258.

FLEMING, R. H., 1939. The control of diatom populations by grazing. *J. Cons. int. Explor. Mer*, 14, 210-227.

FORSTER, G. R., 1953. Peritrophic membranes in the Caridea (Crustacea Decapoda). *J. Mar. biol. Ass. U.K.*, 32, 315-318.

Fox, H. M., 1937. The activity and metabolism of poikilothermal animals in different latitudes. I: *Proc. zool. Soc. Lond.*, 1936, 945-955.

Fox, H. M., 1939. The activity and metabolism of poikilothermal animals in different latitudes. V: *Proc. zool. Soc. Lond.*, A, 109, 141-156.

Fox, H. M., 1952. Anal and oral intake of water by crustacea. *J. exp. Biol.*, 29, 583-599.

Fox, H. M., and Wingfield, C. A., 1937. The activity and metabolism of poikilothermal animals in different latitudes. II: *Proc. zool. Soc. Lond.*, A, 275-282.

Friedrich, H., 1931. Mittheilungen über vergleichende Untersuchungen über den Lichtsinne einiger mariner Copepoden. *Z. vergl. Physiol.*, 15, 121-138.

Fuller, J. L., 1937. Feeding rate of *Calanus finmarchicus* in relation to environmental conditions. *Biol. Bull. Wood's Hole*, 72, 233-246.

Fuller, J. L., and Clarke, G. L., 1936. Further experiments on the feeding of *Calanus finmarchicus*. *Biol. Bull. Wood's Hole*, 70, 308-320.

Gaarder, T., 1932. Untersuchungen über Produktions und Lebensbedingungen in norwegischen Austern-pollen. *Bergens Mus. Aarb.*, 64 pp.

Gardiner, A. C., 1933. Vertical distribution in *Calanus finmarchicus*. *J. Mar. biol. Ass. U.K.*, 18, 575-610.

Gauld, D. T., 1951. The grazing rate of planktonic copepods. *J. Mar. biol. Ass. U.K.*, 29, 695-706.

Gauld, D. T., 1953. Diurnal variations in the grazing of planktonic copepods. *J. Mar. biol. Ass. U.K.*, 31, 461-474.

Gibbons, S. G., 1933. A study of the biology of *Calanus finmarchicus* in the northwestern North Sea. *Fisheries, Scot., Sci. Invest.*, 1933, 1, 24 pp.

Gibbons, S. G., 1936. *Calanus finmarchicus* and other copepods in Scottish waters in 1933. *Fisheries, Scot., Sci. Invest.*, 1936, 2, 37 pp.

Giesbrecht, W., 1892. Systematik und Faunistik der pelagischen Copepoden des Golfes von Neapel und der angrenzenden Meeres-abschnitte. *Fauna u. Flora Neapel*, 19, 1-831.

Goodsir, H. D. S., 1843. Account of the maidre of the fishermen, and descriptions of some new species of crustaceans. The genus *Cetochilus* belonging to the order Copepoda and the family *Pontia* of M. Edwards. On a new genus and species of crustacean. *Edinb. New Phil. J.*, 35, 102-104, 336-339.

Gran, H. H., 1902. Das Plankton des norwegischen Nordmeeres von biologischen und hydrographischen Gesichtspunkten behandelt. *Rep. Norweg. Fish. Invest.*, 2, No. 5, 222 pp.

Gran, H. H., 1929. Quantitative plankton investigations carried out during the expedition with the 'Michael Sars', July-Sept. 1924. *Rapp. Cons. Explor. Mer*, 56, 50 pp.

Gray, J., 1928. *Ciliary movement*. Cambridge.

Grobben, C., 1881. Die Entwicklungsgeschichte von *Cetochilus septentrionalis* Goodsir. *Arb. zool. Inst. Univ. Wien*, 3, 1-40.

Gross, F., and Raymont, J. E. G., 1942. The specific gravity of *Calanus finmarchicus*. *Proc. roy. Soc. Edinb.*, B, 61, 288-296.

Gunnerus, J. E., 1770. Nogle smaa rare mestendelen nye norske Sødyr beskrevene. *Skr. Kiöbenhavnske Selsk. Laerd. og Videnskab. Elsk.*, 1765-1769, 10, 175.

GUNTER, G., WILLIAMS, R. H., DAVIS, C. C., and WALTON SMITH, F. G., 1948. Catastrophic mass mortality of marine animals and coincident phytoplankton bloom on the west coast of Florida, November, 1946-August, 1947. *Ecol. Monogr.*, 18, 309-324.

GUNTHER, E. R., 1934. Observations on the fatty constituents of marine plankton. I: Biology of the plankton. *J. exp. Biol.*, 11, 173-197.

GURNEY, R., 1929. Dimorphism and rate of growth in copepods. *Int. Rev. Hydrobiol.*, 21, 189-207.

GURNEY, R., 1931. *British fresh-water copepoda.* Vol. 1, Ray Society, London.

HALL, R. E., 1953. Observations on the hatching of eggs of *Chirocephalus diaphanus* Prévost, *Proc. zool. Soc. Lond.*, 123, 95-109.

HANSEN, K. V., 1951. On the diurnal migration of zooplankton in relation to the discontinuity layer. *J. Cons. int. Explor. Mer*, 17, 231-241.

HARDING, J. P., MARSHALL, S. M., and ORR, A. P., 1951. Time of egg laying in the planktonic copepod *Calanus. Nature*, 167, 953.

HARDY, A. C., 1924. The herring in relation to its animate environment. Part I: The food and feeding habits of the herring with special reference to the east coast of England. *Fish. Invest., Lond.*, Ser. II, 7, No. 3, 53 pp.

HARDY, A. C., 1936. The continuous plankton recorder. *'Discovery' Rep.*, 11, 457-510.

HARDY, A. C., 1941. Plankton as a source of food. *Nature*, 147, 695.

HARDY, A. C., 1943-44. 'Plankton as food' in *Rep. Scot. Mar. biol. Ass.*, 8-9.

HARDY, A. C., 1953. 'Some problems of pelagic life' in *Essays in marine biology*, Edinburgh.

HARDY, A. C., and BAINBRIDGE, R., 1951. Effect of pressure on the behaviour of decapod larvae (Crustacea). *Nature*, 167, 354.

HARDY, A. C., and BAINBRIDGE, R., 1954. Experimental observations on the vertical migrations of plankton animals. *J. Mar. biol. Ass. U.K.*, 33, 409-448.

HARDY, A. C., and GUNTHER, E. R., 1935. The plankton of the South Georgia whaling ground and adjacent waters, 1926-27. *'Discovery' Rep.*, 11, 1-456.

HARDY, A. C., and PATON, W. N., 1947. Experiments on the vertical migration of plankton animals. *J. Mar. biol. Ass. U.K.*, 26, 467-526.

HARRIS, J. E., 1953. Physical factors involved in the vertical migration of plankton. *Quart. J. micr. Sci.*, 94, 537-550.

HARTOG, M., 1888. The morphology of *Cyclops* and the relations of the Copepoda. *Trans. Linn. Soc. Lond. (Zool.)*, Ser. 2, 5, 1-46.

HARVEY, H. W., 1934. Annual variation of planktonic vegetation, 1933. *J. Mar. biol. Ass. U.K.*, 19, 775-792.

HARVEY, H. W., 1937. Note on selective feeding by *Calanus. J. Mar. biol. Ass. U.K.*, 22, 97-100.

HARVEY, H. W., 1942. Production of life in the sea. *Biol. Rev.*, 17, 221-246.

HARVEY, H. W., 1950. On the production of living matter in the sea off Plymouth. *J. Mar. biol. Ass. U.K.*, 29, 97-137.

HARVEY, H. W., COOPER, L. H. N., LEBOUR, M. V., and RUSSELL, F. S., 1935. Plankton production and its control. *J. Mar. biol. Ass. U.K.*, 20, 407-442.

HARVEY, J. M., 1930. The action of light on *Calanus finmarchicus* (Gunner.) as determined by its effect on the heart beat. *Contr. Canad. Biol.*, 5, 83-92.

HASLER, A. D., 1937. The physiology of digestion in planktonic crustacea. II: Further studies on the digestive enzymes of (A) *Daphnia* and *Polyphemus*, (B) *Diaptomus* and *Calanus*. *Biol. Bull. Wood's Hole*, 72, 290-298.

HEBERER, G., 1924. Die Spermatogenese der Copepoden. I: Die Spermatogenese der Centropagiden nebst Anhang die Oogenese der *Diaptomus castor*. *Z. wiss. Zool.*, 142, 191-253.

HEBERER, G., 1932a. Die Spermatogenese der Copepoden. II: Das Conjugations und Reduktionsproblem in der Spermatogenese der calanoiden Copepoden mit einem Anhang über die Spermatogenese von *Sapphirina ovatolanceolata* (Dana). *Z. wiss. Zool.*, 123, 555-646.

HEBERER, G., 1932b. Untersuchungen über Bau und Funktion der Genitalorgane der Copepoden. I: Der männliche Genitalapparat der calanoiden Copepoden. *Z. mikr.-anat. Forsch.*, 31, 250-424.

HEBERER, G., 1937. Weitere Ergebnisse über Bildung und Bau der Spermato-phoren und Spermatophorenkoppelapparate bei calanoiden Copepoden. *Verh. dtsch. zool. Ges.*, 39, 86-93.

HENSEN, V., 1887. Ueber die Bestimmung des Planktons. 5 *Ber. Komm. Wiss dtsch. Meere*, 1-108.

HERDMAN, W. A., 1919. Spolia Runiana. III: The distribution of certain diatoms and Copepoda, throughout the year, in the Irish Sea. *J. Linn. Soc. Lond. (Zool.)*, 34, 95-126.

HEYERDAHL, THOR, 1950. *The Kon-Tiki expedition*. London.

HILTON, I. F., 1931. The oogenesis of *Calanus finmarchicus*. *Quart. J. micr. Sci.*, 74, 193-222.

HJORT, J., 1933. Essays on population. Whales and whaling. *Hvalråd. Skr.*, 7, 1-7.

HJORT, J., and RUUD, J. T., 1929. Whaling and fishing in the North Atlantic. *Rapp. Cons. Explor. Mer*, 56, 123 pp.

HOVASSE, R., 1925. Les Ellobiopsidés se propagent par flagellispores. *C. R. Acad. Sci. Paris*, 181, 196-198.

HOVASSE, R., 1951. Contributions à la connaissance biologique des Ellobiopsidae; la sporulation chez *Ellobiopsis fagei* sp. nov. *C. R. Acad. Sci. Paris*, 233, 980-982.

HUNTSMAN, A. G., 1924. Limiting factors for marine animals. I: The lethal effect of sunlight. *Contr. Canad. Biol.*, N.S., 2, 83-88.

HUNTSMAN, A. G., and SPARKS, M. L., 1925. Limiting factors for marine animals. III: Relative resistance to high temperatures. *Contr. Canad. Biol.*, N.S., 2, 95-114.

JASCHNOV, W., 1939. Plankton productivity of the south-western part of the Barents Sea, from '50 Cruises of the Research Ship Persey'. *Trans. Inst. Mar. Fish.*, U.S.S.R., 4, 201-224.

JASCHNOV, W. A., 1939. Reproduction and seasonal variations in the distribution of different stages of *Calanus finmarchicus* of the Barents Sea, from '50 Cruises of the Research Ship Persey'. *Trans. Inst. Mar. Fish.*, U.S.S.R., 4, 225-244.

JEPPS, M. W., 1937a. On the protozoan parasites of *Calanus finmarchicus* in the Clyde sea area. *Quart. J. micr. Sci.*, 79, 589-658.

JEPPS, M. W., 1937b. Note on Apstein's parasites and some very early larval Platyhelminthes. *Parasitology*, 29, 554-558.

JESPERSEN, P., 1928. Investigations on the food of the herring in Danish waters. *Medd. Komm. Havundersøg., Kbh.*, Ser. Plankton, 2, No. 2, 150 pp.

JESPERSEN, P., 1932. On the food of the herring in Icelandic waters. *Medd. Komm. Havundersøg., Kbh.*, Ser. Plankton, 2, No. 3, 34 pp.

JESPERSEN, P., 1934. The Godthaab expedition. Copepoda. *Medd. Grønland*, 79, No. 10, 166 pp.

JESPERSEN, P., 1939a. Investigations on the copepod fauna in East Greenland waters. *Medd. Grønland*, 119, No. 9, 106 pp.

JESPERSEN, P., 1939b. The zoology of East Greenland. Copepods. *Medd. Grønland* 121, No. 3, 66 pp.

JOYEUX, C., 1922. Recherches sur l'*Urocystis prolifer* Villot. Note préliminaire. *Bull. Soc. zool. Fr.*, 47, 52-58.

KEYS, A. B., 1930. The measurement of the respiratory exchange of aquatic animals. *Biol. Bull. Wood's Hole*, 59, 187-198.

KLEM, A., 1932. Contribution to the study of the oils of marine crustacea. I: The oils of *Meganyctiphanes norvegica*, M. Sars, and *Calanus finmarchicus*, Gunn. *Hvalråd. Skr.*, No. 6, 24 pp.

KLUGH, A. B., 1929. The effect of the ultra-violet component of sunlight on certain marine organisms. *Canad. J. Res.*, 1, 100-109.

KLUGH, A. B., 1930. The effect of the U.V. component of light on certain aquatic organisms. *Canad. J. Res.*, 3, 104.

KRAEFFT, F., 1910. Über das Plankton in Ost- und Nordsee und den Verbindungs-gebieten, mit besonderer Berücksichtigung der Copepoden. *Wiss. Meeresun-tersuch., Abt. Kiel*, 11, 29-107.

KROGH, A., 1931. Dissolved substances as food of aquatic organisms. *Biol. Rev.*, 6, 412-442.

KROGH, A., 1941. *Comparative physiology of respiratory mechanisms*. Philadelphia, 1941.

KRØYER, H., 1848. Karcinologiske Bidrag (Fortsaettelse): Slaegten *Calanus*. *Naturhistorisk Tidskrift*, 1846-49, 527-560.

LANG, K., 1947. A contribution to the question of the mouth parts of the Copepoda. *Ark. Zool.*, 38, 1-24.

LEACH, W. E., 1819. Entomostracés. Article in *Dictionnaire Sc. Nat.*, Strasbourg and Paris, 14, 524-543.

LEBOUR, M. V., 1916. Stages in the life history of *Calanus finmarchicus* (Gunnerus), experimentally reared by Mr L. R. Crawshay in the Plymouth laboratory. *J. Mar. biol. Ass. U.K.*, 11, 1-17.

LEBOUR, M. V., 1921. The food of young clupeoids. *J. Mar. biol. Ass. U.K.*, 12, 458-467.

LEBOUR, M. V., 1922. The food of plankton organisms. *J. Mar. biol. Ass. U.K.*, 12, 644-677.

LEBOUR, M. V., 1923. The food of plankton organisms. II. *J. Mar. biol. Ass. U.K.*, 13, 70-92.

LEBOUR, M. V., 1924. The food of young herring. *J. Mar. biol. Ass. U.K.*, 13, 325-330.

LINDERSTRØM-LANG, K., 1937. Principle of the Cartesian diver applied to gasometric technique. *Nature*, 140, 108.

LOVERN, J. A., 1935. Fat metabolism in fishes. VI: The fats of some plankton crustacea. *Biochem. J.*, 29, 847-849.

LOWE, E., 1935. The anatomy of a marine copepod *Calanus finmarchicus* (Gunnerus). *Trans. roy. Soc. Edinb.*, 58, 561-603.

LOWNDES, A. G., 1935. The swimming and feeding of certain Calanoid copepods. *Proc. zool. Soc. Lond.*, 687-715.

LOWNDES, A. G., 1942. The displacement method of weighing living aquatic organisms. *J. Mar. biol. Ass. U.K.*, 25, 555-574.

LUCAS, C. E., 1938. Some aspects of integration in plankton communities. *J. Cons. int. Explor. Mer*, 13, 309-322.

MANTEUFEL, B. P., 1941. Plankton and herring in the Barents Sea. *Trans. Knipovich polyar. Sci. Inst.*, 7, 125.

MARSHALL, S., 1924. The food of *Calanus finmarchicus* during 1923. *J. Mar. biol. Ass. U.K.*, 13, 473-479.

MARSHALL, S. M., 1933. On the biology of *Calanus finmarchicus*. II: Seasonal variations in the size of *Calanus finmarchicus* in the Clyde sea area. *J. Mar. biol. Ass. U.K.*, 19, 111-138.

MARSHALL, S. M., 1949. On the biology of the small copepods in Loch Striven. *J. Mar. biol. Ass. U.K.*, 28, 45-122.

MARSHALL, S. M., NICHOLLS, A. G., and ORR, A. P., 1934. On the biology of *Calanus finmarchicus*. V: Seasonal distribution, size, weight and chemical composition in Loch Striven in 1933 and their relation to the phytoplankton. *J. Mar. biol. Ass. U.K.*, 19, 793-828.

MARSHALL, S. M., NICHOLLS, A. G., and ORR, A. P., 1935. On the biology of *Calanus finmarchicus*. VI: Oxygen consumption in relation to environmental conditions. *J. Mar. biol. Ass. U.K.*, 20, 1-28.

MARSHALL, S. M., NICHOLLS, A. G., and ORR, A. P., 1937. On the growth and feeding of the larval and post-larval stages of the Clyde herring. *J. Mar. biol. Ass. U.K.*, 22, 245-267.

MARSHALL, S. M., NICHOLLS, A. G., and ORR, A. P., 1939. On the growth and feeding of young herring in the Clyde. *J. Mar. biol. Ass. U.K.*, 23, 427-455.

MARSHALL, S. M., and ORR, A. P., 1927. The relation of the plankton to some chemical and physical factors in the Clyde sea area. *J. Mar. biol. Ass. U.K.*, 14, 837-868.

MARSHALL, S. M., and ORR, A. P., 1952. On the biology of *Calanus finmarchicus*. VII: Factors affecting egg production. *J. Mar. biol. Ass. U.K.*, 30, 527-547.

MARSHALL, S. M., and ORR, A. P., 1953. *Calanus finmarchicus*: egg production and egg development in Tromsø Sound in spring. *Acta Borealia*, A, 5, 21 pp.

MARSHALL, S. M., and ORR, A. P., 1954. Hatching in *Calanus finmarchicus* and some other copepods. *J. Mar. biol. Ass. U.K.*, 33, 393-410.

MARSHALL, S. M., ORR, A. P., and REES, C. B., 1953. *Calanus finmarchicus* and related forms. *Nature*, 171, 1163.

MARUKAWA, H., 1921. Plankton list and some new species of copepods from the northern waters of Japan. *Bull. Inst. océanogr. Monaco* No. 384, 15 pp.

MATTHEWS, L. H., and PARKER, H. W., 1950. Notes on the anatomy and biology of the basking shark. *Proc. zool. Soc. Lond.*, 120, 553-576.

MILLAIS, J. G., 1904-06. *The mammals of Great Britain and Ireland.* London.

MILNE-EDWARDS, H., 1840. *Histoire naturelle des crustacés comprenant l'anatomie, la physiologie et la classification de ces animaux.* 3 vols., Paris, 1834-1840.

MÜLLER, O. F., 1776. Zoologiae Danicae prodromus, Havniae.

MÜLLER, O. F., 1785. Entomostraca seu Insecta Testacea quae in aquis Daniae et Norvegiae reperit, descripsit et iconibus illustravit. Lipsiae et Havniae, 134 pp., 21 T.

MUŽINIĆ, S., 1931. Der Rhythmus der Nahrungsaufnahme beim Hering. *Ber. dtsch. Komm. Meeresforsch.*, 6, 62-64.

NATHANSOHN, A., 1909. Sur les relations qui existent entre les changements du plankton végétal et les phénomènes hydrographiques. *Bull. Inst. océanogr. Monaco*, No. 140, 94 pp.

NAUMANN, E., 1923. Spezielle Untersuchungen über die Ernährungsbiologie des tierischen Limnoplanktons. II: Über der Nahrungserwerb der Copepoden und der Rotiferen des Limnoplanktons. *Lunds Univ. Årsskr.* (2), 19 (6).

NICHOLLS, A. G., 1933a. On the biology of *Calanus finmarchicus.* I: Reproduction and seasonal distribution in the Clyde sea area during 1932. *J. Mar. biol. Ass. U.K.*, 19, 83-110.

NICHOLLS, A. G., 1933b. On the biology of *Calanus finmarchicus.* III: Vertical distribution and diurnal migration in the Clyde sea area. *J. Mar. biol. Ass. U.K.*, 19, 139-164.

NIELSEN, E. STEEMANN, 1934. The production of phytoplankton at the Faroe Isles, Iceland, East Greenland and in the waters around. *Medd. Komm. Havunder- søg., Kbh.*, Ser. Plankton, 3, 93 pp.

NIELSEN, E. STEEMANN, 1937. On the relation between the quantities of phytoplankton and zooplankton in the sea. *J. Cons. int. Explor. Mer*, 12, 147-155.

NIKITIN, W. N., 1931. Die untere Planktongrenze und deren Verteilung im Schwarzen Meer. *Int. Rev. Hydrobiol.*, 25, 102-130.

NIKITINE, B., 1929. Les migrations verticales saisonnières des organismes planktoniques dans la mer Noire. *Bull. Inst. océanogr. Monaco*, 540, 24 pp.

NORDGAARD, O., 1905. *Hydrographical and biological investigations in Norwegian fjords.* Bergen.

NORMAN, J. R., and FRASER, F. C., 1937. *Giant fishes, whales and dolphins.* London.

OBERG, M., 1906. Die Metamorphose der Plankton-Copepoden der Kieler Bucht. *Wiss, Meeresuntersuch. Abt. Kiel*, 9, 37-175.

OGILVIE, H. S., 1927. Observations on the food of post-larval herring from the Scottish coast. *Fisheries, Scot., Sci. Invest.*, No. 1, 10 pp.

OGILVIE, H. S., 1934. A preliminary account of the food of the herring in the north-western North Sea. *Rapp. Cons. Explor. Mer*, 89, 85-92.

ORR, A. P., 1934. On the biology of *Calanus finmarchicus.* IV: Seasonal changes in weight and chemical composition of *Calanus* from Loch Fyne. *J. Mar. biol. Ass. U.K.*, 20, 613-632.

OSTENFELD, C. H., 1913. De danske Farvandes Plankton i Aarene 1898-1901. III: Phytoplankton og Protozoer. *K. danske vidensk. Selsk., Raekke* 7, *Naturvid. afd.*, 9, 113.

OSTVEDT, O. J., 1953. Zooplankton investigations from Weather Ship M in the Norwegian Sea, 1948-49. II: The annual vertical migration and its role in the life history of copepods. *Hvalråd. Skr.*, 40.

PAULSEN, O., 1906. Studies in the biology of *Calanus finmarchicus* in the waters round Iceland. *Medd. Komm. Havundersøg., Kbn.*, Ser. Plankton, 1, 21 pp.

PÜTTER, A., 1907a. Die Ernährung der Wassertiere. *Z. allg. Physiol.*, 7, 283-320.

PÜTTER, A., 1907b. Der Stoffhaushalt des Meeres. *Z. allg. Physiol.*, 7, 321-368.

PÜTTER, A., 1909. *Die Ernährung der Wassertiere und der Stoffhaushalt der Gewässer.* Jena.

PÜTTER, A., 1922. Die Frage der parenteralen Ernährung der Wassertiere. *Biol. Zbl.*, 42, 72-86.

PÜTTER, A., 1923. Der Stoffwechsel der Copepoden (zugleich ein Beispiel für die Verwendung der Korrelations-methode in der Physiologie). *Pflüg. Arch. ges. Physiol.*, 201, 503-536.

PÜTTER, A., 1924-25. Die Ernährung der Copepoden. *Arch. Hydrobiol.*, 15, 70-117.

RADOVICH, J., 1952. Food of the Pacific sardine *Sardinops caerulea* from central Baja California and Southern California. *Calif. Fish Game*, 38, 475-477.

RAYMONT, J. E. G., and GAULD, D. T., 1951. The respiration of some planktonic copepods. *J. Mar. biol. Ass. U.K.*, 29, 681-693.

RAYMONT, J. E. G., and GROSS, F., 1942. On the breeding and feeding of *Calanus finmarchicus* under laboratory conditions. *Proc. roy. Soc. Edinb.*, B, 61, 267-287.

REES, C. B., 1949. Continuous plankton records: the distribution of *Calanus finmarchicus* (Gunn.) and its two forms in the North Sea, 1938-39. *Hull Bull. Mar. Ecol.*, 2, 215-275.

REVERBERI, G., and PITOTTI, M., 1943. Il ciclo biologico e la determinazione fenotipica del sesso di *Ione thoracica* Montagu. Bopiride parassita di *Callianassa laticauda* Otto. *Pubbl. Staz. zool. Napoli*, 19, 111-184.

RILEY, G. A., 1946. Factors controlling phytoplankton populations on Georges Bank. *J. Mar. Res.*, 6, 54-73.

RILEY, G. A., 1947a. A theoretical analysis of the zooplankton population of Georges Bank. *J. Mar. Res.*, 6, 104-113.

RILEY, G. A., 1947b. Seasonal fluctuations of the phytoplankton population in New England coastal waters. *J. Mar. Res.*, 6, 114-125.

RILEY, G. A., and VON ARX, R., 1949. Theoretical analysis of seasonal changes in the phytoplankton of Husan Harbour, Korea. *J. Mar. Res.*, 8, 60-72.

RILEY, G. A., and BUMPUS, D. F., 1946. Phytoplankton and zooplankton relationships on Georges Bank. *J. Mar. Res.*, 6, 33-47.

RILEY, G. A., and GORGY, S., 1948. Quantitative studies of summer plankton populations of the western North Atlantic. *J. Mar. Res.*, 7, 100-121.

RILEY, G. A., STOMMEL, H., and BUMPUS, D. F., 1949. Quantitative ecology of the plankton of the western North Atlantic. *Bull. Bingham océanogr. Coll.*, 12, 3, 169 pp.

Rose, M., 1925. Contribution à l'étude de la biologie du plankton; le problème des migrations verticales journalières. *Arch. Zool. exp. gén.*, 64, 387-549.

Rose, M., 1929. Copépodes pélagiques particulièrement de surface provenant des campagnes scientifiques de S. A. S. le Prince Albert 1er de Monaco. *Résult. Camp. sci. Monaco*, 78, 132 pp.

Rose, M., 1933. Copépodes pélagiques. *Faune de France*, 26, Paris.

Runnstrøm, S., 1932. Eine Uebersicht über das Zooplankton des Herdla und Hjeltefjordes. *Bergens Mus. Aarb.*, No. 7, 67 pp.

Russell, F. S., 1925. The vertical distribution of marine macroplankton. An observation on diurnal changes. *J. Mar. biol. Ass. U.K.*, 13, 769-809.

Russell, F. S., 1926. The vertical distribution of marine macroplankton. The apparent importance of light intensity as a controlling factor in the behaviour of certain species in the Plymouth area. *J. Mar. biol. Ass. U.K.*, 14, 415-440.

Russell, F. S., 1927. The vertical distribution of plankton in the sea. *Biol. Rev.*, 2, 213-262.

Russell, F. S., 1928a. The vertical distribution of marine macroplankton. VI: Further observations on diurnal changes. *J. Mar. biol. Ass. U.K.*, 15, 81-99.

Russell, F. S., 1928b. The vertical distribution of marine macroplankton. VII: Observations on the behaviour of *Calanus finmarchicus*. *J. Mar. biol. Ass. U.K.*, 15, 429-454.

Russell, F. S., 1930a. Do oceanic plankton animals lose themselves? *Nature*, 125, 17.

Russell, F. S., 1930b. Vitamin content of marine plankton. *Nature*, 126, 472.

Russell, F. S., 1934a. The vertical distribution of marine macroplankton. XII: Some observations on the vertical distribution of *Calanus finmarchicus* in relation to light intensity. *J. Mar. biol. Ass. U.K.*, 19, 569-584.

Russell, F. S., 1934b. The zooplankton. III: A comparison of the abundance of zooplankton in the Barrier Reef lagoon with that of some regions in northern European waters. *Sci. Rep. Gr. Barrier Reef Exped.*, 2, 176-185.

Russell, F. S., 1951. A re-examination of *Calanus* collected off Plymouth. *J. Mar. biol. Ass. U.K.*, 30, 313-314.

Ruud, J. T., 1929. On the biology of copepods off Møre, 1925-27. *Rapp. Cons. Explor. Mer*, 56, 57 pp.

Sars, G. O., 1903. *An account of the crustacea of Norway.* IV: *Copepoda calanoida.* Bergen.

Savage, R. E., 1930. The influence of *Phaeocystis* on the migrations of the herring. *Fish. Invest. Lond.*, Ser. 2, 12, No. 2, 14 pp.

Savage, R. E., 1931. The relation between the feeding of the herring off the east coast of England and the plankton of the surrounding waters. *Fish. Invest. Lond.*, Ser. 2, 12, No. 3, 88 pp.

Scoresby, W., 1820. *An account of the Arctic regions.* 2 vols. Edinburgh.

Scott, T., 1887. Notes on the contents of the stomachs of herring and haddocks. *6th Ann. Rep. Fish Bd Scot.*, p. 225.

Scott, T., 1897. The marine fishes and invertebrates of Loch Fyne. *15th Ann. Rep. Fish Bd, Scot., Sci. Invest.*, 107-174.

SEWELL, R. B. SEYMOUR, 1912. Notes on the surface living Copepoda of the Bay of Bengal. I and II. *Rec. Indian Mus.*, N.S., 7, 313-382.

SEWELL, R. B. SEYMOUR, 1929 and 1932. The Copepoda of Indian seas. Calanoida. *Mem. Indian Mus.*, 10, 1-382.

SEWELL, R. B. SEYMOUR, 1947. The free-swimming planktonic Copepoda. *Sci. Rep. Murray Exped.*, 8, 1-303.

SEWELL, R. B. SEYMOUR, 1951. The epibionts and parasites of the planktonic Copepoda of the Arabian Sea. *Sci. Rep. Murray Exped.*, 9, 255-394.

SOLEIM, P., 1942. Årsaker til rike og fattige årganger ar sild. *Fiskeridir. Skr. Havundersøk.*, 7, No. 2, 39 pp.

SØMME, J., 1934. Animal plankton of the Norwegian coast waters and the open sea. I: *Fiskeridir. Skr. Havundersøk*, 4, No. 9, 1-163.

SPOONER, G. M., 1933. Observations on the reactions of marine plankton to light. *J. Mar. biol. Ass. U.K.*, 19, 385-438.

STALBERG, G., 1931. Eine *Calanus* Form aus dem Telezker See im Altai. *Zool. Anz.*, 95, 209-220.

STØRMER, L., 1929. Copepods from the 'Michael Sars' expedition 1924. *Rapp. Cons. int. Explor. Mer*, 56, 57 pp.

USSING, H. H., 1938. The biology of some important plankton animals in the fjords of East Greenland. *Medd. Grønland*, 100, 1-108.

VANE, F. R., 1952. The distribution of *Blastodinium hyalinum* in the North Sea. *Challenger Soc.*, 3, No. 4, 23-24.

VAUZÈME, ROUSSEL DE, 1834. Description du *Cetochilus australis*, nouveau genre de Crustacé Branchiopode. *Ann. Sci. nat.*, 1, 333-338.

VERWOORT, W., 1951. Plankton copepods from the Atlantic sector of the Antarctic. *Verh. Akad. Wet. Amst., Afd. Nat.*, 47, 1-156.

WAILES, G. H., 1936. Food of *Clupea pallasii* in southern British Columbia waters. *J. biol. Bd Can.*, 1, 477-486.

WIBORG, K. F., 1934. The production of zooplankton in the Oslo Fjord in 1933-34 with special reference to the copepods. *Hvalråd. Skr.*, No. 21, 87 pp.

WIBORG, K. F., 1954. Investigations on zooplankton in coastal and offshore waters of western and north-western Norway with special reference to the copepods. *Fiskeridir. Skr. Havundersøk.*, 2, 246 pp.

WILLEY, A., 1919. Report on the Copepoda obtained in the Gulf of St. Lawrence and adjacent waters, 1915. *Can. Fish. Exp.*, 1914-1915, 173.

WILSON, C. B., 1932. The copepods of the Woods Hole region, Massachusetts. *Bull. U.S. nat. Mus.*, 158, 1-635.

WILSON, C. B., 1942. The copepods of the plankton gathered during the last cruise of the Carnegie. *Sci. Res. Cr. VII, Carnegie, Biol.* 1, 1-237.

WIMPENNY, R. S., 1937. The distribution, breeding and feeding of some important plankton organisms of the south-west North Sea in 1934. Part I: *Calanus finmarchicus* (Gunn.), *Sagitta setosa* (J. Müller) and *Sagitta elegans* (Verrill). *Fish. Invest. Lond.*, Ser. 2, 15, No. 3, 53 pp.

WIMPENNY, R. S., 1938. Diurnal variation in the feeding and breeding of zooplankton related to the numerical balance of the zoo-phyto-plankton community. *J. Cons. int. Explor. Mer*, 13, 323-337.

REFERENCES

WITH, C., 1915. Copepoda I. Calanoida Amphascandria. *Dan. Ingolf. Exped.*, 3, 1-248.

WOLFENDEN, R. N., 1905. Notes on the Copepoda of the North Atlantic sea and the Faroe Channel. *J. Mar. biol. Ass. U.K.*, 7, 110-146.

YONGE, C. M., 1938. The nature and the significance of the membranes surrounding the developing egg of *Homarus vulgaris* and other Decapoda. *Proc. zool. Soc. Lond.*, A, 107, 1937, 499-517.

YUDANOVA, O. N., 1940. Khimicheskii Sostav *C. finmarchicus* Barentsova Motya. *Dokl. Akad. Nauk. S.S.S.R.*, N.S. 29, No. 3, 218-224.

ZEUTHEN, E., 1947. Body size and metabolism rate in the animal kingdom with special regard to the marine micro-fauna. *C.R. Carlsberg, Ser. Chem.*, 26, 17-161.

INDEX

Numbers italicized refer to figures